D0926090

Mastercraftsmen of Ancient Peru

ALAN R. SAWYER

Published by The Solomon R. Guggenheim Foundation, New York, 1968
Library of Congress Card Catalogue Number: 68-56627

LENDERS TO THE EXHIBITION

NATIONAL INSTITUTIONS

Museo Nacional de Antropología y Arqueología, Pueblo Libre.
*MNA *Dr. Jorge C. Muelle, Director.*

Museo Arqueológico Bruning, Lambayeque.
MBL *Dr. Oscar Fernandez de Cordova, Director.*

Museo de Arqueología, Universidad Nacional de Trujillo.
MAT *Dr. Jorge Zevallos Quinones, Director.*

Instituto de Antropología y Agricultura Precolombiana,
Universidad Agraria del Perú.
IAA *Dr. Frederick Engel, Director.*

Museo Arqueológico, Gran Unidad Escolar Santa Isabel, Huancayo.
HYO

Museo Histórico de Ayacucho,
AYO *Dr. Cesar O. Prado Paredes, Director.*

Museo Regional de Ica,
MRI *Dr. Adolfo Bermudez Jenkins, Director.*

PRIVATE COLLECTIONS

The names of the owners are listed after the title of the collection when different

HA	Honorato Amado	Lima-Nazca
MA	Museo Amano *Yoshitaro Amano*	Lima
RA	Raul Apesteguia	Lima
LC	Luis Camino	Lima-Palpa
AC	J. Alex Ciurlizza	Lima
HC	Hugo Cohen Collection *Elsa Letts de Cohen*	Lima
SD	Sixtilio Dalmau	Lima
EG	Elena Gaffron	Lima
GG	Guillermo Ganoza	Trujillo
TG	Toto Giurato	Lima

**These abbreviations are used throughout the checklist to indentify the lender*

WG	Walter Gross	Lima
ML	Museo Larco Herrera *Isolina de Larco* *Isabel Larco de Alvarez Calderon* *Carola Larco de Sarria*	Lima
MM	Manuel Mujica Gallo	Chosica
EN	Eugenio Nicolini Iglesias	Lima
JP	Juan Luis Pereira	Lima
AR	Aldo Rubini Drago	Ocucaje
CS	Carlos Soldi Collection *Ana Maria de Soldi*	Lima
ES	E. A. Sellschopp	Lima
DS	Domingo Seminario Urrutia	Lima-Piura
FS	Fritz Smischek	Trujillo
GS	Gonzalo del Solar	Lima
SZ	Fernando de Szyszlo	Lima
FT	Felipe Thorndike	Lima-Chosica
PT	Paul Truel	Lima-Ocucaje
HZ	Harold Zoeger Silva	Pimentel-Chiclayo

SUPPLEMENTARY LOANS

ANON	Eight anonymous private collectors	The United States Brazil Argentina
AMNH	American Museum of Natural History	New York City
AICG	The Art Institute of Chicago (Gaffron Collection)	Chicago
TMDC	The Textile Museum	Washington, D. C

ACKNOWLEDGEMENTS

The Solomon R. Guggenheim Museum ordinarily chooses to devote its exhibition and publication program to painting and sculpture of the *modern era*, a designation intended to comprise the last hundred years, from the emergence of Impressionism to our time. MASTERCRAFTSMEN OF ANCIENT PERU as here presented is, therefore, an innovation as well as an experiment which the Foundation's Trustees approved as a possible precursor to other exhibitions surveying the creative richess of a particular, now historic, civilization. Peru seemed a promising subject to begin such visual inquiries, for its many levelled Pre-Columbian cultures, stretching partly in chronological, partly overlapping sequences through centuries, are mirrored in objects which become, simultaneously, carriers of a great episode in the civilization of mankind and an autonomous achievement speaking through its perfection to modern sensibilities.

For the purposes of the current exhibition project, more than 600 objects, large and small, representational and decorative, functional and symbolic, in stone, wood, metal, clay and in fabric, have been assembled from divergent sources to constitute the most comprehensive such view of Peru's collective genius ever attempted. An exhibition of such scope is always an undertaking that depends upon the generous participation of many, variously qualified individuals. This is even more true with a subject that lies beyond the Museum's curatorial competence and of a project that required years of search and preparation in distant parts of the world, outside the bounds and conventions of a familiar art world. Thus, to a more exclusive degree than with subjects more familiar to us, the curatorial responsibility for this exhibition was placed in the hands of a specialist in the field. Dr. Alan Sawyer, Director of The Textile Museum in Washington, D.C. and Peruvian scholar, was one of the few individuals to whom this show and its accompanying catalogue could be safely entrusted, and who therefore was appointed curator of the exhibition.

Dr. Sawyer, on his frequent journeys through the Peruvian lands was accompanied by staff members of the Guggenheim Museum, partly to assist with the securing of loans, but chiefly to inject the Museum's presence in the inevitably complex and highly responsible negotiations with lenders, museums, and government officials, who in concert with the curator of the exhibition and with our administrative staff gradually cleared the formidable obstacles to the project. Special thanks are due to Everett Ellin, formerly Assistant to the Director, and to Orrin H. Riley, Conservator, who during the past three years spelled each other in the completion of this task. Mr. Riley, in addition, must be credited with having devised methods through which the safe transfer of objects could be assured, first from the far reaches of Peru to a central gathering point in Lima, and eventually from the Peruvian capital to New York City. The last phase of Mr. Riley's contribution is the installation on the ramps of the Frank Lloyd Wright building which through its ready adaptation to yet another untried exhibition type proved again its great versatility under conditions of competent planning and execution.

It would have been more convenient to rely on sources of easy access, but it was decided in the initial exhibition phases, to avoid expedients so as to arrive at an exhibition based almost wholly upon material previously unseen in this country. The lending burden, therefore, rested heavily upon the country of origin where twenty-five private individuals and seven National Museums, in full awareness of the cultural significance of this event, went far beyond the bounds of normal participation, as they decided to part for more than standard exhibition time with objects of uncommon rarity and beauty.

Even so, there is reason to doubt, that MASTERCRAFTSMEN OF ANCIENT PERU could have been presented at the Guggenheim Museum, had it not been possible to count on the most consistent and effective support from the highest authorities in the country of origin. We are greatly indebted to His Excellency, President Fernando Belaunde Terry and His Excellency, Ambassador Celso Pastor de la Torre for their unfailing support throughout the four years during which this exhibition has been in preparation.

Others in both Peru and the United States made, at various times, decisive contributions towards the success of the exhibition. Not to exceed the format of this brief roster of acknowledgements their part must be mentioned in much abbreviated fashion although not without sincere gratitude for invaluable services rendered. Among Lima citizens ever ready to furnish needed guidance and assistance, were in particular Walter Gross, Alex Ciurlizza and other members of the Institute of Contemporary Art, Manuel Checa Solari, Carmen Gonzales, Elena Gaffron, Juana Truel, Gene Savoy, Pedro Rojas Ponce and Gonzalo del Solar.

Mr. Ciurlizza and Manual Ulloa took an active part in obtaining, through private subscription funds, a scholarship enabling a Peruvian student to join the project here and thereby derive useful instruction in Museum methods eventually to be applied in his own country.

William Kaplan offered many hours of his time and skill to aid the Guggenheim Museum in the preparation of the works for exhibition.

I wish to acknowledge gratefully financial contributions made in the form of free and reduced services by the Official Tourist Bureau, Grace Lines, Braniff International Airlines, Eastern Airlines, Faucett Airlines, The Hotel Crillon, and Ford Motor Company. We are also appreciative of the care and efficiency of the Peruvian investigation police in safeguarding the loans during their assembly.

A few desired loans could not be negotiated in Peru and thanks are due to eight anonymous private collectors of the United States, Brazil and Argentina together with the American Museum of Natural History in New York, The Art Institute of Chicago and The Textile Museum of Washington, D.C. for select supplementary loans.

It would be unjust not to mention in closing the quietly effective part played by all Museum Departments in the staging of MASTERCRAFTSMEN OF ANCIENT PERU, an exhibition that will, within our ranks, be long remembered as one of the most exacting and rewarding ever presented.

THOMAS M. MESSER, Director
The Solomon R. Guggenheim Museum

INTRODUCTION

The Spanish conquistadors of the early 16th Century were tough, determined, and resourceful men, stripped of tolerance and compassion by the Inquisition and hardened by Spain's bitter struggle to drive the Moslems from their homeland. They were fired by the adventurer's lust for easy riches and had but slight awareness of the great intellectual and artistic achievements of the civilizations they destroyed. Beautifully wrought ritual objects of gold and silver were melted down. Exquisitely woven textiles and beautifully fashioned objects of ceramic and other materials were cast aside as worthless or destroyed in iconoclastic zeal.

After the splendid kingdoms of Mexico and Central America had been sacked in rapid succession, enriching the participants beyond imagination and sending a steady stream of treasure back to mother Spain, those who had not yet made their fortunes turned southward to the fabled realm of the Incas. The conquest of Peru was swift and final. In 1532 Francisco Pizarro landed at Tumbes, just south of the present Ecuadorian border, with less than 200 followers. Within a few months he had captured the Inca Atahualpa by treachery, exacted a huge ransom, and put him to death. Then, reinforced by 150 men under Diego de Almagro, he quickly routed the native armies, disorganized by the loss of their absolute ruler, and methodically set about looting the great cities of the Inca Empire. By 1536 the last organized resistance was crushed. In the fighting among the victors over the spoils both Almagro and Pizarro met death.

Throughout the Colonial period that followed, the treasure hunt went on. The land was divided among the victors and favorites of the Spanish crown while the population was forced to work the mines and ransack the temples and cemeteries of their ancestors for precious metals. Attempts by the crown to lay claim to the treasure were largely ignored as were its administrative reforms aimed at protecting the Indians. In 1780 a widespread insurrection led by Tupac Amaru II was brutally suppressed. In 1820 Peru joined its neighboring South American colonies in a successful revolt against Spain, leaving the country solidly under the control of the landowners.

Meanwhile, in Europe and North America the end of the 18th Century saw a great reawakening of interest in antiquity stimulated by Winckelmann's discoveries at Herculaneum and Pompeii and the archeological plunder brought back by Napoleon's soldiers after their invasion of Egypt. Inevitably this new wave of interest spread to the long overlooked ancient civilizations of the Americas.

John Lloyd Stethens and Frederick Catherwood began their trail blazing explorations of Maya ruins in 1839. The sensation created by the publication of their *Incidents of Travel in Yucatan* was closely followed by that stirred by William H. Prescott's thoroughly researched and eminently readable *The Conquest of Mexico*. In 1847 his equally remarkable *The Conquest of Peru* appeared, focusing public attention for the first time in three centuries on the ancient heritage of that remote and almost forgotten land.

In 1863 the famed pioneer American archeologist Ephriam George Squier arrived in Peru and for 3 years traveled throughout the coast and highlands filling notebooks with accurate observations and detailed plans of ancient ruins. His profusely illustrated account, *Peru: Incidents of Travel and Exploration in the Land of the Incas,* published in 1877, laid the cornerstone of Peruvian archeology.

The interest and involvement of the scholarly community in ancient Peruvian studies gradually increased during the remainder of the 19th Century. It culminated in the extensive excavations conducted by Max Uhle in the 1890's and the early years of this century, for various American institutions. In addition to materials brought back by archeologists, large collections of Peruvian antiquities that had been gathered by hacienda owners, foreign residents, and travelers, found their way into European and American museums.

In 1911 Hiram Bingham startled the world with his discovery of Machu Picchu. Two years later the Peruvian government established its National Museum of Anthropology and Archeology under the directorship of Dr. Julio C. Tello. The appearance of this dedicated and gifted man on the Peruvian archeological scene could not have been more timely. With extraordinary energy he conducted reconnaissance and excavation of ancient sites throughout the length and breadth of Peru and assembled at the National Museum the largest and most comprehensive collection of Peruvian antiquities in the world. His sensational discoveries stimulated an ever-increasing number of Peruvian and foreign archeologists to turn their talents and energies toward unveiling the mysteries of Peru's past. After his death in 1947 his spirit continued to be a primary source of inspiration to those who followed in his footsteps.

The role that the private collector has played in Peruvian art and archeology cannot be minimized. Almost invariably he has freely shared his collection and his knowledge with the archeologist and art historian and in some cases has developed outstanding scholarship in his own right. This was particularly true of Don Rafael Larco Hoyle, founder of the Larco Herrera Museum, whose contribution to our knowledge of Peruvian prehistory ranks second only to that of Dr. Tello. Most Peruvian collectors have been closely associated with the land from which their collections derived. Their interest has tended to be strongly antiquarian though they were also moved by the esthetic qualities of their possessions. In recent years their ranks have been joined by an increasing number of art-oriented collectors located principally in Lima. Together they hold an important segment of the nation's historic treasure.

With the advent of the collector in the 19th Century, a new profession was created, that of the "huaquero" or pot hunter. He was a direct descendant of the colonial laborer used by the landowner in his search of precious metals. Now he was employed in the systematic looting of ancient cemeteries not only for objects of gold and silver, which had come to be worth more as art than as precious metal, but for pottery, textiles and other artifacts. As the demand increased, greater profits were to be realized and the huaqueros soon began digging clandestinely on their own. A new wave of pillage spread across the land compounding the damage to ancient sites wrought by colonial treasure hunters.

In their hasty probing for saleable objects, the huaqueros not only destroyed or seriously damaged fragile materials but irrevocably lost information important to the scholar such as association and provenience. Tello had the practice outlawed in 1930 but it has been difficult to control, especially in sparsely populated rural areas. The problem resembles that of the sorcerer's apprentice. Today the looting still goes on, aided and abetted by public indifference, a rising art market, and the depressed economic status of the lower class. "Huaqueando" is about the only means its members have of breaking the grip of poverty. It is a sad fact that, in spite of the dedicated efforts of many archeologists, the majority of ancient Peruvian art objects in public and private collections of the world today derived from huaquero activity.

As the twentieth century has progressed, there has been an ever-increasing awareness of the artistic as well as the archeological aspects of Peruvian antiquities. Because of the relative inaccessibility of Peru before the advent of air travel, however, world recognition of the art of ancient Peru has tended to lag somewhat behind that of Mexico and Central America. It was not until the 1950's that it began to be given its rightful place in art museums beside objects representing other great art traditions. In 1952 The Art Institute of Chicago placed on exhibition the famous collection of Dr. Edward Gaffron assembled in Peru during the 19th Century and made famous through German publications. It was soon to form the founding acquisition of the Institute's Department of Primitive Art — the first such department established in a major art museum. In 1954 the Museum of Modern Art presented its renowned "Ancient Arts of the Andes" show which included objects from all the western South American countries, assembled by René d'Harnoncourt from sources in Europe, the United States, and South America. The exhibition travelled to Minneapolis and San Francisco.

In 1955 Peru sent an exhibition of ancient, colonial, and modern Peruvian art to Mexico City and Toronto followed by a larger exhibit of the same type shown in 1957 in Paris. Since that time there have been numerous exhibitions of varying size and emphasis in museums throughout the world. The present exhibition is the largest, most comprehensive and, we believe, the most selective ever assembled of those limited to the country's ancient heritage. It has been drawn almost entirely from seven national museums and twenty-six private collections in Peru. A large proportion of the objects shown have never before been exhibited or published outside the country.

GEOGRAPHY

To understand the complexity of Ancient Peruvian cultural history one must begin with an awareness of the country's diverse and hostile geography. Formidable physical barriers tended to separate the population into more or less isolated groups. Progress towards civilization was the result of the ancient Peruvians' organized efforts to survive and prosper within the harsh limitations of their environment. A brief discussion of the three principal geographical zones of Peru will afford the reader an understanding of the character of the ancient civilizations they produced and some comprehension of the problems facing the modern researcher in his attempts to reconstruct the history of these areas.

THE COAST

The most accessible and best known area of Peru is its narrow coastal plain cut at uneven intervals by about forty river valleys. These valleys vary considerably in size, and in the amount of water their rivers bring down from the mountains. Some streams flow to the sea all year round, while others furnish water for a relatively short period. In ancient times survival depended on the efficient use of water by irrigation and the stock piling of staple foods such as corn and beans against long periods of drought. The climate was ideal but life was always precarious. Natural disasters such as flash floods or earthquakes could destroy cities and irrigation systems without warning, and the population had to be constantly alert against armed invasion by peoples from less fortunate climes. Even the sea, an important source of food, was subject to unpredictable cycles of fecundity.

Quite naturally, the more extensive and well watered valleys, which could support large populations, became the homes of the more advanced ancient civilizations. Groups of valleys in close geographic proximity tended to form federations for greater economic and military security. Population centers were concentrated along the valley's desert margins and on land elevated above the broad intensively cultivated valley floor. Preference was given to sites that were easily defensible and further protection was afforded by strategically placed walls and garrisoned fortifications. Since rains were rare and no threat to adobe building, most construction was of that material.

Because of their wealth and accessibility, the coastal cities were among the first to be sacked during the conquest, and during the colonial treasure hunt and subsequent huaquero activity scarcely a coastal site large or small escaped being plundered. Architectural remains not destroyed in the pillage have suffered from earthquakes and wind-driven sand. In the north they have also been eroded by infrequent rains. Yet there is one great compensation to the archeologist faced with such handicaps. The preservation of archeological materials in the arid sandy wastes of the coast is remarkable. Fragile textiles, feather work and other perishable materials are often found in almost perfect condition.

Strange as it may seem, many of the largest and most impressive ruins on the coast are among the least understood. Their thorough study will require sustained archeological campaigns such as have characterized the archeology of the Mediterranean area but which have not yet been initiated in Peru.

THE HIGHLANDS

The second important geographical zone of Peru is composed of the incredibly rugged Central Andes crowded with peaks rising as high as 22,205 feet above sea level. To the north, the zone is comparatively narrow and is made up of ranges running roughly parallel to the coast. These broaden out in the central highlands

and in the south form a vast high plateau much of which is barren and inhospitable.
Water is plentiful throughout much of this zone but, because of the high altitude and harsh topography, only a few of the more extensive highland basins and intermountain valleys were capable of supporting large unified populations. Life in the highlands was and is hard. Floods, landslides, and earthquakes are an ever present menace. The practice of agriculture is difficult and travel is arduous in the rugged terrain and lung-bursting altitudes, yet the Andean Indian long ago became well adapted to his strenuous environment. His carefully terraced fields climb up the mountain sides to 16,000 feet and higher, and a vast network of trails traverses the steep scarps and mountain ridges where modern roads cannot follow. The ruins of countless well constructed stone cities and fortifications give eloquent testimony to the organization, skill, and tenacity of the ancient population. As we shall soon see, three times in the history of ancient Peru highland peoples were able to bring all, or nearly all, of the Central Andean area under their sway.
Much of the highland area has been explored by archeologists but physical hardship has limited their excavations to a few samplings in some of the more accessible areas. Little is known of the regional cultures that lay outside the temporal span and sphere of influence of the three major Pan-Andean civilizations and even the history and origin of these is shrouded in mystery. Not only is the work of the archeologist more difficult in the highlands but it is much less rewarding in terms of well preserved art objects than on the coast. Perishable materials such as textiles survive only under the most fortuitous circumstances.

THE EASTERN SLOPES

The third archeologically important zone of Peru is made up of the jungle-shrouded eastern slopes of the Andes. It is an area of heavy rainfall where deeply cut valleys drop abruptly in altitude as they merge with the upper Amazon basin. For many years the zone was thought to be archeologically unimportant on the grounds that its dense tropical vegetation was incompatible with highland agricultural techniques.
Persistent reports of large and impressive jungle cities tended to be ignored until in recent years the well documented and widely publicized discoveries of the American explorer Gene Savoy prodded the archeologists into action. Now an increasing number of scientific incursions into the zone have been made and excited reports of new discoveries follow in rapid succession. It is obvious that the area developed distinctive regional cultures of its own. Few ceramic styles have yet been identified and perishable materials do not survive, but the architecture shows a preference for circular forms as opposed to the generally rectangular tradition of the highlands.
In the vicinity of Pucallpa on the eastern limits of the zone, Donald Lothrop has conducted excavations which reveal a long unbroken sequence of highly sophisticated cultures in the area. Some of his earlier levels suggest relationships to the site of Kotosh in the Central Andes recently excavated by the University

of Tokyo. As the eastern slopes of the Andes are opened up to the outside world by President Belaunde's new marginal highway, we may expect an ever increasing number of important discoveries. Some may revolutionize our thinking about the origin and evolution of ancient Andean civilization.

SUMMARY

After a century of archeological investigation, the broad outlines of ancient Peruvian cultural history in the coastal valleys are known, though our knowledge is far from complete. Only a few highland centers have been investigated and much remains to be done before we will fully understand the history and character of ancient civilizations in this important area. Of the eastern slopes of the Andes we know almost nothing other than its important potential as an area for future research.

The exhibition, like the collections from which it is drawn, places vastly disproportionate emphasis on the coastal zone, and therefore gives a distorted impression of ancient Andean civilizations. This is inevitable, not only because of the unequal attention the zones have received from archeologists (and the huaquero) but on account of drastically different conditions affecting the survival of archeological materials.

In selecting objects for the exhibition, the curator has placed primary emphasis on esthetic quality while at the same time seeking to present the major aspects of ancient Peruvian art. Special attention was given to major art styles such as Chavin and Vicus which have not previously been shown in quantity outside Peru. Ceramics, because of their consistent survival, make up the bulk of the show. Through the courtesy of the Trustees of The Textile Museum in Washington, D.C., some of the finest textiles in Peruvian collections have been cleaned and mounted for the exhibition under the supervision of their conservation staff. Many of the finest objects of gold in Peruvian collections recently toured the United States and most owners were therefore reluctant to lend them again after so short an interval of time.

In the catalog of the exhibition that follows, the listing of each group of objects is preceded by a brief résumé of their cultural background. Space does not permit a discussion of the many problems of chronology and cultural relationship which engage the Peruvianist. The curator has therefore had to state his interpretations without qualifying argument.

PROLOGUE

Peru's earliest inhabitants were nomadic bands of Stone Age hunters, fishermen, and food gatherers who roamed the coast and highlands between seven and twelve thousand years ago and perhaps earlier. Subsequent occupation of the more inhabitable areas have obliterated all traces of their campsites but artifacts have been found in ancient shell middens along the Pacific shore, in highland caves, and in once verdant areas of the coastal desert left desolate by climate change. One such area is the Pampa de los Fosiles in the barren Cupisnique Quebrada located in the desert between the Chicama and Jequetepeque Valleys on the north coast.

1. Three stone implements, Pampa de los Fosiles, Cupisnique, Quebrada, 10,000–5,000 B.C. FS *
   A. Projectile point, black stone, 3⅛″ long.
   B. Leaf-shaped scraper, yellow grey stone, 4″ long.
   C. Boat-shaped scraper, grey stone, 4¾″ long.
2. Two stone implements. Pampa de los Fosiles, Cupisnique, Quebrada, 10,000–5,000 B.C. ANON
   A. Projectile point, grey stone, 4⅛″ long.
   B. Leaf-shaped blade, grey stone, 5½″ long.

* *See lenders list for full name, pp. 6–7.*

THE EARLIEST PERUVIAN ART

From about 5,000 to 3,000 B.C. there was a gradual transition throughout the central Andean area from the nomadic way of life to the establishment of permanent settlements utilizing domesticated plants and animals to supplement wild food supplies. At the site of one such community on the north coast, Huaca Prieta in the Chicama Valley, Dr. Junius B. Bird discovered the earliest known art objects of Peru.

The stratified refuse of Huaca Prieta yielded a large number of fragments of twined cotton textiles that Dr. Bird has shown, through careful analysis of their warp movements, to have been ornamented with highly stylized bird, animal, human, and other motifs. He also found the fragile remains of two small beautifully carved gourds which, because of their dissimilarity to other excavated materials, he has suggested were importations to the site. The surprising degree of sophistication in the designs of both the textiles and the gourds indicate that a considerable period of cultural development had preceded them.

3. Twined cotton textile with design of condor, $8\frac{1}{2} \times 4\frac{1}{4}$". Pre Ceramic Period, about 2,500 B.C. Huaca Prieta, Chicama Valley. AMNH
4. Small gourd carved with anthropomorphic figures. The lid is ornamented with an S shaped device ending in bird heads. $2\frac{3}{8}$" diameter. Pre Ceramic Period, about 2,500 B.C., Huaca Prieta, Chicama Valley. AMNH

THE EARLY CERAMIC PERIOD

The earliest known ceramics from Peru are dated around 2,000 B.C. By 1,500 B.C. the basic techniques of reduction and oxidation firing and modes of decoration such as incising, painting, and the use of clay slip were all being practiced. The following examples were excavated by Dr. Bird at a site close by Huaca Prieta.

5. Clay stamp in the form of a bird, probably for decorating textiles. Red pigment, $1\frac{1}{2}$" h. Early Ceramic Period, about 1,500 B.C., Chicama Valley. AMNH
6. Solid clay figurine of seated hunchback, $2\frac{5}{8}$" h. Early Ceramic Period, about 1,500 B.C., Chicama Valley. AMNH

19

THE ART OF CHAVIN

The first great civilization of Peru crystalized in the northern highlands around 1,200 B.C. It is called Chavin after the most famous of its ceremonial centers at Chavin de Huantar, a little town in the Mosna Valley, one of the southernmost branches of the large Marañon Valley that bisects the Northern Andes. Another elaborate temple complex called Pacopampa is located over 200 miles to the north-west in the western reaches of the Marañon drainage. Many other Chavin sites have been found in the area between and in the valleys of the north coast. The influence of Chavin religion and its distinctive art style has been traced northward into Ecuador and south along the coast as far as the Nazca Valley, a span of 1,000 miles.

In the light of present knowledge, the Chavin culture appeared suddenly, full grown, advanced in the arts and architecture, and motivated by a dynamic religion. This had led to speculation as to its possible relationships with the Chou Dynasty in China and the Olmec civilization of Mexico, both of which were contemporary. Chavin art features jungle creatures such as the jaguar, cayman, and serpent, and it is possible that the original home of the Chavin people may someday be found hidden under the dense tropical foliage of the little explored eastern slopes of the Andes.

16

HIGHLAND CHAVIN STONE CARVINGS

The symbolism of Chavin art is best displayed in the superb reliefs and carvings that ornamented the culture's principal stone structures. The basic elements are few: jaguar, human, bird of prey, cayman, and serpent, but they are combined with infinite complexity into apparitions of powerful supernatural beings. Since many of these carvings are massive and could not be moved, we supplemented our examples with rubbings taken from the originals by Fred D. Ayers, and lent to us by the American Museum of Natural History. The Chavin style is thought to have covered a period of about 800 years. Exact chronological relationships have not yet been established and our dates are therefore expressed in broad tentative terms.

EARLY CHAVIN, 1,200–1,000 B.C.

7. Relief showing figure of man in profile holding trophy head in right hand. Rhyolite porphyry, 19⅞ x 16⅝ x 4⅞". Olayan, Mosna Valley. EG
8. Fragment (top) of stella showing profile heads of anthropomorphic feline on each side. Rhyolite porphyry, 16⅛ x 11⅜ x 5¾". Runtu, Mosna Valley. MM
9. Tenoned head of serpent with feline fangs. Rhyolite porphyry, 21 x 14 x 11½". Chavin de Huantar. ML
10. Rubbing of stone relief representing a bat, 19½ x 21½". Chavin de Huantar. AMNH
11. Rubbing of stone relief representing an eagle. 19¾ x 19⅛". Chavin de Huantar. AMNH

MIDDLE CHAVIN, 1,000–700 B.C.

12. Rubbing of stone relief representing an anthropomorphic feline with serpent tresses holding fish (?) and spondylus shell in hands. 20⅞ x 22¾". Chavin de Huantar. AMNH
13. Rubbing of stone frieze of mythical eagles and falcons. 20 x 192". Chavin de Huantar. AMNH
14. Rubbing of relief on stone column representing an anthropomorphic falcon. 89½ x 74¼". Chavin de Huantar. AMNH
15. Rubbing of relief on stone column, representing an anthropomorphic eagle. 89½ x 74¼". Chavin de Huantar. AMNH

*16. Relief fragment showing head of mythical falcon. Rhyolite porphyry, 16½ x 11⅞ x 5¼". Runty, Mosna Valley. MM

17. Relief fragment showing head of mythical eagle. Ryolite porphyry, 21¼ x 14½ x 6¼". Chavin de Huantar. MM
18. Relief fragment showing foot and breast of mythical bird or jaguar. Rhyolite porphyry, 12⅞ x 17¾ x 5¾". Chavin de Huantar. MM

* *illustrated*

MASTERCRAFTSMEN OF ANCIENT PERU

Co-sponsored at the Los Angeles County Museum of Art by Braniff International Airlines and the Marcona Corporation

MASTERCRAFTSMEN OF ANCIENT PERU has come to Los Angeles through the swift and vigorous action of a network of people — for the most part mutually unacquainted — in the incredibly short period of three months. It was in early December we first heard, as a result of the unprecedented success of the exhibition in New York, that the Peruvian leaders might be willing to extend their loans to one other city in the United States. The Trustees immediately endorsed our hope that Los Angeles would be that city and the staff began optimistically revising the spring exhibition schedule. Thomas Messer, Director of The Solomon R. Guggenheim Museum, flew to Peru to discuss the matter with Peruvian officials, museum directors and private collectors. In early January he cabled the generous approval of the Peruvian lenders.

While the total staff became involved immediately in transferring the exhibition of more than seven hundred objects from New York to Los Angeles, designing and executing a completely new installation and planning attendant activities, the Trustees attacked the problem of finding supplemental funds necessary to present an unscheduled show of this magnitude. Henry Mudd spoke with Charles W. Robinson, President of the Marcona Corporation, and Franklin Murphy approached Harding Lawrence, President of Braniff International Airlines. The presidents conferred and reported that they welcomed the opportunity to co-sponsor this exhibition in California "as a means of strengthening the cultural and social bonds between the people of Peru and the people of the United States."

We have therefore many people to thank for the opportunity of presenting this exhibition at the Los Angeles County Museum of Art. It is with great pleasure that we extend our appreciation to His Excellency, President General Manuel Velazco Alvarado, to His Excellency, Ambassador Fernando Berckmeyer and to Dr. Pedro Garcia Miró, Director of the Corporacion de Turismo for their endorsement of the exhibition; to the generous lenders: the museum directors and private collectors in Peru and their counterparts in Argentina, Brazil and the United States; to Harding Lawrence and Charles W. Robinson and the boards of their corporations; to Thomas Messer and his staff at the Guggenheim Museum; to Henry Mudd and Franklin Murphy of our Board of Trustees; and to the members of our own staff who have worked weekends and evenings to have the exhibition open on time.

KENNETH DONAHUE, Director

*19. Sculpture in round of jaguar. Limestone, $24\frac{3}{4} \times 34\frac{1}{2} \times 25\frac{1}{2}$″. Pacopampa. ML

20. Mortar and pestle. Andesite porphyry, mortar, $3\frac{1}{8}$″ h., $4\frac{5}{8}$″ diameter, in the form of a mythical feline-eagle. The pestle, $4\frac{1}{8}$″ long, bears the head of a serpent. Pacopampa. ML

21. Miniature tenoned head of anthropomorphic feline. Rhyolite porphyry, $3\frac{7}{8}$″ h. Chavin de Huantar. MNA

LATE CHAVIN, 700–500 B.C.

22. Fragment of relief showing plumage of mythical bird. Slate, $17\frac{1}{2}$″. Chavin de Huantar. MNA

29

CHAVIN MINOR ARTS

The selected group of Chavin ceramics and other objects in the exhibition is almost all from the north coast valleys of Peru. Most are without exact provenience and their chronological relationships are not certain. They are arranged in groups according to their probable age and regional substyle.

EARLY CHAVIN ART, 1,200–1,000 B.C.

Stirrup spout bottles, provenience unknown, unless otherwise indicated.

23. Gold repoussé pendant in the form of a crouching feline. 3x4″, 17 gm. Chongoyape, Lambayeque Valley (?) TMDC

*24. Bottle with incised feline-eagle. (Note similarity to figure 23, except for beak and wing.) Grey ware, $8\frac{3}{4}$″ h. Chicama Valley (?) FT

25. Bottle, owl head. Greyware, $8\frac{1}{2}$″ h. Vicus, Piura Valley. DS

26. Gold head band with repoussé feline head. $7\frac{1}{2}$″ diameter, $1\frac{3}{4}$″ h. HC

27. Bottle, relief of mythical eagle in profile. Blackware, $8\frac{7}{8}$″ h. Chicama Valley (?) MAT

28. Bottle, relief of mythical eagle with wings outspread. Blackware, 9″ h. HC

*29. Bottle, relief of mythical bird head. Brownware with graphite, $8\frac{1}{4}$″ h. DS

30. Single spout bottle with incised abstract symbol. Blackware, $9\frac{1}{8}$″ h. AMNH

31. Effigy jar in form of standing monkey. Brownware, $9\frac{1}{8}$″ h. MNA

32. Bottle, curvilinear bands in relief. Redware with graphite, $9\frac{1}{8}$″ h. DS

33. Bottle, ribbed stirrup and body. Brownware with yellow patina, $8\frac{1}{8}$″ h. DS

34. Bottle, circles in relief. Black-brownware with graphite, $7\frac{1}{4}$″ h. ML

35. Bottle, four feline heads in bold relief. Blackware, $9\frac{1}{8}$″ h. MA

36. Bottle, textured surface representing plumage (?) Blackware, $9\frac{3}{4}$″ h. Chongoyape, Lambayeque Valley. WG

THE CHAVIN ART OF CHONGOYAPE

A number of Chavin style gold objects have been found in the vicinity of Chongoyape in the Lambayeque Valley. By comparison with Highland Chavin stone monuments, most may be assigned to the Middle Chavin period. Ceramics found in the same area are characterized by the skillful use of surface texture, and are usually non-religious in subject matter. The examples listed here are tentatively assigned to the same period as the gold.

MIDDLE CHAVIN, 1,000–700 B.C., CHONGOYAPE

Stirrup spout bottles of dark grey ware, unless otherwise indicated

37. Gold repoussé plaque with standing frontal figure of an anthropomorphic feline with serpent tresses. (Compare with # 12.) 4¼ x 8¾″, 96 gm. TMDC
38. Pair of gold ear spools with repoussé anthropomorphic feline faces. 2⅝″ diameter. ANON
39. Bottle, seated rat (stirrup spout missing), 7″ h. ANON
40. Bottle, rat seated on muffin form, 8″ h. DS
41. Drum-shaped bottle with stepped fret device in relief. 9¼″ h. DS

*42. Bottle, owl seated on hemispherical form. 9″ h. ANON
43. Bottle, seated man, hand to mouth. 9⅛″ h. ANON
44. Bottle, polished circles against textured background. 8¾″ h. DS

THE CHAVIN ART OF CUPISNIQUE

Sr. Raphael Larco gave the name Cupisnique to north coast Chavin ceramics after finding sherds of the type in the Cupisnique Quebrada in 1933. Most ceramics of the style have been found in the Chicama Valley at sites such as Sausal. This selection all dates from the Late Chavin period.

LATE CHAVIN, 700–500 B.C., CUPISNIQUE

45. Head jar, old man with wrinkled face. Greyware, 6⅜″ h. Chicama Valley. ML
46. Single spout bottle with mace form. Greyware, 10⅛″ h. Chicama Valley. ML
47. Single spout bottle with finely incised and textured surface. Dark greyware, 8⅞″ h. Moche Valley (?) MAT
48. Bottle, puma in high relief against background of rocks and cactus. Brownware with traces of cream slip, 11⅜″ h. Provenience unknown. ANON
49. Globular bottle with twisted rope form at top and incised abstract mythical being. Grey ware, 11″ h. Provenience unknown. ANON
50. Bottle, fine line incised motifs. Blackware, 10⅛″ h. Moche Valley (?) MAT
51. Stone mace head with four flaring blades with pairs of spikes between. Form derived from cactus (?) Rhyolite porphyry, traces of red paint, 4¼″ h. Chicama Valley. ML.
52. Stone mace head with parallel diagonal blades. 3⅜″ h. Chicama Valley. AMNH

24 42 54

THE CHAVIN ART OF TEMBLADERA

In recent years a large number of Chavin ceramics and stone artifacts have appeared on the market which are said to have come from the vicinity of Tembladera in the Jequetepeque Valley. The style is contemporary with, and very similar to that of, Cupisnique, but tends to be more flamboyant with greater emphasis on religious subjects. This might be explained by its close proximity to the important Chavin ceremonial center at Kuntur Wasi (La Copa) higher up in the Jequetepeque Valley. Evidently, there is an absence of ground water at the burial sites since paints applied after firing are often well preserved. (They were also used on Cupisnique and other Chavin pottery styles, but seldom survive.)

LATE CHAVIN, 700–500 B.C., TEMBLADERA

53. Head cup, anthropomorphic feline face. Blackware, traces of red paint, 4⅜″ h. AC
*54. Bottle, kneeling hunchback, serpent incised on back. Blackware, well preserved red and white paint, 10″ h. ANON
55. Effigy jar, seated hunchback. Blackware with traces of red paint, 6″ h. RA
56. Single spout bottle with flange in the form of a mythical fish. Dark brownware, traces of red and white paint, 11″ h. DS
57. Bottle, mythical serpent with feline head. Dark brownware, wel preserved red, orange and white paint. ANON
58. Bottle, seated feline. Grey brown ware, traces of red paint, 10½″ h. ANON
59. Bottle, modeled eagle forming part of its spout. Incised anthropomorphic feline heads on body of vessel. Dark brownware, traces of red paint, 11⅛″ h. ANON
60. Bottle, an acrobat lying on his stomach, his feet touching the back of his head. Dark greyware, 9¼″ h. ANON
61. Three clay whistles, each with two stops giving them three distinct tones. Greyware with traces of paint. DS
    A. Human figure form, 2¾″ long.
    B. Human head form, 1⅝″ long.
    C. Human leg form, 1⅝″ long.
62. Whistle in form of woman with holes at breasts serving as stops. Greyware, traces of paint, 3″ h. ANON
63. Cylinder seal and two clay stamps. Brownware. Such stamps are rare in ancient Peru, and Tembladera is one of the few sites at which they have been found (see #5). ANON
    A. Cylinder, when rolled forms band of feline heads alternating in direction.
    B. Stamp, anthropomorphic feline head with tripart headdress.
    C. Stamp, anthropomorphic feline head surrounded by scroll elements.
64. Miniature jar, form of a rhinoceros beetle. Brownware, 2¼″ h. x 5¼″ long. ANON.
65. Miniature stone cup, incised anthropomorphic feline heads with tripart headdresses. Tan, red paint in the incisions, type of soapstone, 1¼″ h. DS
66. Shallow stone bowl, flaring sides. Low relief on exterior consisting of frontal face and strap work. Rose tinted, type of soapstone, 1¾″ h., 5½″ diameter. DS
67. Miniature stone double cup, relief of twined fret with anthropomorphic feline heads in centers. Type of soapstone, 1⅝″ h. ANON
68. Three miniature stone vessels. Type of soapstone. DS
    A. Bowl, uncurved rim, rows of bumps on exterior. Buff, 1″ h.
    B. Bowl, uncurved rim. Buff, 1⅛″ h.
    C. Ladle, notched handle, hole in pommel. Pink, 3″ long.
69. Two model ears of corn. DS
    A. Light grey stone, 2⅝″ long.
    B. Black stone, 2⅞″ long.
70. Model ear of corn. Dark grey stone, 4¾″ long. FS
71. Stone figure seated crosslegged with hands clasped at chest. Mottled grey green stone, 2¾″ h. ANON
72. Two undecorated stone mortars with flaring sides, each with pestle. RA
    A. Grey green andesite porphyry, 8¼″ h., 11¾″ diameter, with pestle 9⅞″ long.
    B. Grey green andesite porphyry, 5⅛″ h., 9¼″ diameter, with pestle 6½″ long.

CHAVIN ART IN TRANSITION

Towards the end of the long Chavin period centralized control of the culture waned and Chavin art displayed the strong technological and cultural influences of new groups moving into the north coast area. This change was particularly evident in ceramics which showed a shift to oxidation firing and the use of colored clay slips with traditional incised lines.

LATE CHAVIN TRANSITION, 500–400 B.C.

73. Stone mortar, straight sides, incised with fine lines representing a frontal human figure and abstract architectural (?) elements. The function of the two slotted holes which pierce the figure is not known. Andesite porphyry, $7\frac{5}{8}$″ h., 9″ diameter. MBL
74. Bottle, kneeling man, hair in cylindrical bun, diagonal face marking. Arms incised on body of vessel. Though Chavinoid in style, this attractive ceramic shares many features with contemporary Paracas art on the south coast while its stirrup spout is close in form to those of the first period of the Mochica (Moche) Culture. It is difficult to place the piece as to its area of origin but it probably dates very late in the Chavin period. Finely polished blackware, $7\frac{3}{4}$″ h. HYO
75. Single spout bottle. Red slipped and burnished in zones between vertical ribs, $4\frac{3}{8}$″ h. Tembladera. RA
76. Bottle, incised band of abstract anthropomorphic feline heads. Brownware, red and black slip, 10″ h. Vicus, Piura Valley. HZ
*77. Effigy bottle, standing man arms raised to sides. Orangeware, incised and slip painted, red-orange and black, $8\frac{7}{8}$″ h. Vicus, Piura Valley. HZ
78. Bottle, root vegetable form, incised, abstract Chavin symbol. Brownware, black slip, $8\frac{1}{8}$″ h. Chicama Valley (?). ES
79. Bottle, incised stylized anthropomorphic heads. Orangeware, cream and black slip, $11\frac{5}{8}$″ h. Provenience unknown. DS
80. Single spout effigy bottle, seated man half covered by garment. Heavy red and cream slip, $8\frac{1}{2}$″ h. Provenience unknown. ANON
81. Bottle, head incised detail one half of face covered by hairlock. Orange-brownware, red and cream slip, $9\frac{6}{8}$″ h. Vicus, Piura Valley. DS
82. Bottle, stylized spondylus shell. Zone burnished blackware, $7\frac{1}{4}$″ h. Chicama Valley (?) MNA

The stirrup and spout forms of this and the following two pieces place them at the very end of the transition period.

83. Bottle mace head form (see # 52). Light greyware, $7\frac{3}{4}$″ h. Chicama Valley. ANON
84. Orangeware bottle, crayfish, painted in red and cream slip, $8\frac{1}{4}$″ h. Chicama Valley. ANON
85. Female figure with incised detail. Highly polished yellow brownware with black pigment applied to hair, $19\frac{3}{4}$″ h. Curyacu, Central Coast. MNA

THE ART OF VICUS

Six years ago huaqueros encountered ancient burials in the upper Piura Valley near a hill called Cerro Vicus on the hacienda Pabur. Their discovery touched off one of the greatest flurries of huaquero activity in recent times. Literally thousands of graves were opened and today the vast cemetery lies depleted, looking like a World War I battlefield.

The flood of art materials which appeared on the market as a result of this new find has caused great excitement and no little confusion among Peruvianists. A bewildering variety of art objects is represented with some clear relationships to, and many striking differences from, previously known ancient Peruvian art styles. Ceramics can now be assigned with some degree of certainty to phases within two cultural periods: Classic Vicus, and Negative Vicus. Many gold, copper, and stone objects are, however, still difficult to place in their proper chronological context.

The owner of the hacienda Pabur, Sr. Domingo Seminario, unable to control the activities of the huaqueros, began buying the finest of the Vicus materials as soon as they appeared and today has the largest and richest collection of the styles in the world. Almost our entire selection is derived from this source.

THE CLASSIC VICUS CERAMIC STYLE, 400 B.C.-100 A.D.

The Classis Vicus ceramic style is closely related in many ways to that of the early periods of the Mochica culture found in the Chicama and Moche Valleys some 200 miles to the south. The northern varient is, however, superior from both a technical and artistic point of view. The range of its subject matter, while overlapping, is far wider and it shows a greater preference for sculptural rather than painted pottery. The historical relationship between the two centers is as yet not understood and we know litlte about the early periods in the extensive valleys which lie between them. The dates and phase designations used in our discussion here are, therefore, tentative. The Classic Vicus culture may prove to be the parent of Mochica.

CLASSIC VICUS CERAMICS, CHAVINOID PHASE, 400-300 B.C.

The early phase of Classic Vicus ceramics is strongly Chavinoid and may well be at least partly contemporary with the final transitional period. Chavin ceramics are found at Vicus (Nos. 25, 76, 77, 79, and 81) and a nearby site called Morropon. The Chavinoid phase style is characterized by strongly modeled forms and fine line incised detail. A preference is shown for black or greyware, but some mauve and orangewares decorated with cream slip as well as incising, do occur.

Stirrup spout bottles, unless otherwise indicated

*86 Seated man, powerfully modeled face, feline fangs. A prototype of the Mochica god "Ai Apec". Dark greyware, incised detail, 7⅛" h. DS

87. Seated figure, head of vampire bat (?) In Mochica and later context this being is identified as a sky god. (See Nos. 105 and 292.) Dark greyware, incised detail, 7½" h. DS

88. Single spout bottle with strap handle. Two serpents in relief, heads modeled in strong planes suggesting Chavin stone work. Dark greyware, incised detail, 6⅜" h. DS

89. Feline figure in high relief. (Compare with # 48.) Blackware, incised detail, 7⅞" h. DS

90. Seated feline eating snake. Orangeware, cream slip. (Compare with # 89.) 7½" h. DS

91. Seated man holding a jar on his shoulder, (a common subject in this period). The split level hairdo, applied pupils for the eyes, and surface textured by punctating are all Chavin traits. Mauveware, incised and cream slipped detail, 7¾" h. DS

92. Seated man, expressive wrinkled face. Blackware, incised detail, 7⅝" h. DS

93. Reclining deer. Greyware, 7½" h. DS

94. Owl. Greyware, incised detail, 8⅞" h. DS

95. Seated man, animal skin headdress, cape with geometric décor. Blackware, incised detail, 7" h. DS

96 120 86

CLASSIC VICUS CERAMICS, MATURE PHASE, 300–100 B.C.

The term mature is used to indicate the fully developed early Vicus style. The virtuosity of Vicus ceramists was no doubt due in part to the superior clays they had to work with, but their creative genius ranks them among the finest artist craftsmen of ancient Peru.

Stirrup spout bottles

*96. Kneeling warrior, originally inlayed with stone and shell and equipped with miniature copper mace and gold nose ornaments. Orangeware, mauve and cream slip, 6½" h. DS
97. Kneeling warrior, most of stone and shell inlays as well as gold nose ring still in place. It was also equipped with a miniature copper mace. Creamware, 8¼" h. DS
98. Seated man, long aquiline face. Orangeware, red and cream slip, 7⅝" h. DS.
99. Head of old man with wrinkled face, mustache and pointed beard. Creamware, 8⅝" h. DS
100. Seated fat man. Orangeware, nine square grid incised on chest, 7⅝" h. DS
101. Seated man holding lime bottle, strongly modeled face. Buff ware, 7½" h. DS
102. Man standing atop a platform conducting a human sacrifice. (Compare with Mochica II version # 244.) Creamware with touches of red slip, some restorations, 8⅞" h. DS
103. Fledgling condor. Orangeware, cream slip, 7¾" h. DS
104. Male condor. Creamware, mauve slip, 7¼" h. DS
105. Vampire bat. Orangeware, cream slip, 6¼" h. DS
106. One-half of surface ornamented with conical bosses. Blackware, incised detail, 7⅜" h. DS
107. Frog in coils of snake. Creamware, red slip, 7½" h. DS
108. Kneeling llama loaded with bundles of sticks. Creamware, red slip, 6¼" h. DS
109. Kneeling faun. Creamware, 5⅞" h. DS
110. Eared owl. Creamware, red slip, 7⅜" h. DS
111. Hawk standing on eel. Creamware, 8½" h. DS

CLASSIC VICUS CERAMICS, VIRU PHASE, 100 B.C.–100 A.D.

Towards the end of the mature phase, Vicus ceramics began to manifest the strong influence of a culture known as Viru (Gallinazo). This group had appeared on the north coast at the close of the Chavin period and had been displaced in the Chicama and Moche Valleys by the Mochica culture. It was known to have continued in the Viru and other Valleys to the south (see Nos. 191–210), but its movement northward to the Piura Valley had not been suspected. While the Viru culture had little effect on Mochica art, its ceramic style blended smoothly with that of the mature phase of Classic Vicus indicating a peaceful merging of the two traditions.

Ceramics in a pure Viru style are found at Vicus (Nos. 112–116) exhibiting their typical simplified modeling and peculiar long tapering spout and arched tubular handle. Most pieces showing a blending of the two styles have this type of spout and handle (Nos. 117–123), but some have the traditional stirrup spout of Classic Vicus ceramics (Nos. 124–128).

Viru type spouts and handles

112. Owl head on ring based, muffin-shaped vessel. Orangeware, 6⅞" h. DS
113. Man seated on muffin-shaped vessel. Orangeware, 6½" h. DS
114. Seated man holding pottery in hands, casque on back. Orangeware, 6⅜" h. DS
115. Double vessel, standing warrior to front. Creamware, 9⅛" h. DS
116. Standing deer. Orangeware with negative decoration (typical of Viru), 7⅛" h. DS

Viru type spouts and handles

117. Fox eating mouse. Orangeware, cream slip, 5⅞" h. DS
118. Kneeling warrior. Orangeware, cream slip, 8" h. DS
119. Seated man, elaborate headdress, collar of human heads. Orangeware, cream slip, 6⅝" h. DS
*120. Macaw seated atop jar. Orangeware, cream slip, 8⅞" h. DS
121. Monkey standing on all fours. Creamware, 8½" h. DS
122. Double vessel, crayfish atop each, seagull on one. Orange buff ware, 7¾" h. DS
123. Architectural group. Creamware, orange slip, spout missing, 5⅞" h. DS

Stirrup spout bottles

124. Two wrestlers. Creamware, incised detail, 10¾" h. DS
125. Head, geometric face painting. Orangeware, red slip, 9⅜" h. DS
126. Seated man, animal form headdress, geometrically decorated tunic. Orangeware, cream slip, 7¼" h. DS
127. Seated man, grotesque monkey face. Creamware, red slip, 6⅝" h. DS
128. Painted with band of composite bird and feline motifs. Creamware, red brown and orange slip, 6⅛" h. DS

CLASSIC VICUS AND "FRIAS" GOLD

An infinite variety of gold nose ornaments and other objects are reported to have been found at Vicus and at a site called Frias near Ayabaca about 50 miles to the north east in the highlands near the Ecuadorian border. No archeologist has yet visited Frias and there is an unexplained absence of ceramics and other material associated with "Frias gold". Stylistically, there is little to distinguish it from that for which there is more reliable Vicus provenience. While we cannot rule out the existence of other sites, we will treat the gold as one stylistic unit.

It is extremely difficult to relate Vicus gold and ceramic objects stylistically since the two mediums impose quite different limitations on craftsmen. The only evidence we have to go on are actual miniature gold nose ornaments on modeled pottery (# 97), sculptural representations of figures wearing gold ornaments (# 119) and painted motifs on pottery which appear to relate more closely to gold motifs than to the sculptured ones (# 128). An examination of such meagre indications has led to the following hypotheses: that the Classic Vicus culture was skilled at fashioning gold ornaments by soldering together thin sheet gold, twisted gold wire and gold granules; and that the Viru culture introduced the use of repoussé, and bi-metallic (gold and silver or electrum) sheets. As with the ceramics, it is assumed that there was a considerable blending of the two traditions during the Viru phase of the Classic Vicus period.

CLASSIC VICUS GOLD ORNAMENTS, 400 B.C.-100 A.D.

Unless otherwise indicated, provenience is reported to be Vicus.

MATURE PHASE (?) 300–100 B.C.

129. Standing feline, green stone inlay in tail. Soldered construction, twisted wire detail. 1 x 1½", 9.7 gm. DS
130. Crouching feline with pendant from mouth. Soldered construction, twisted wire detail, Frias. ¾ x 1¾", 12.2 gm. HC
131. Grotesque mask with pendant from mouth. Soldered construction gold head, worked and twisted wire detail, Frias. 1⅝ x 1¾", 26.3 gm. HC

*132. Female figure with detachable head. Soldered construction, Frias. 6⅛ x 3½", 60 gm. MBL

133. Six nose ornaments. DS
    - A. Bird form attached. Soldered construction, twisted wire and gold band detail, 1⅝ x 2¼", 7.5 gm.
    - B. Similar but without ornamental detail, 3¼ x 4¼", 20.5 gm.
    - C. Bean-shaped, 1½ x 3⅛", 5.9 gm.
    - D. Filigree work, some holes still contain turquoise inlays, 1¼ x 1⅜", 6.4 gm.
    - E. Filigree work, green stone inlay in center, 1⅛" h., 1¼" diameter, 6 gm.
    - F. Crescent with 21 triangles of fine gold beads on outer edge, 10 conical bosses. Soldered construction, 1⅜ x 1⅞", 5 gm.

VIRU PHASE (?) 100 B.C.-100 A.D.

Mixture of mature and Viru phase Classic Vicus technical traditions.

134. Plumed feline figure ornamenting handle of throwing stick. Bi-metallic plumes and tail. 3¾" h., 79.85 gm. ES
135. Crouching feline, turquoise bead inlays in eyes, shoulders and hips. Soldered construction, twisted wire detail, loop for suspension, 1¼ x 1¾", 11.5 gm. DS
136. Nose ornament, feline head, tail, and two birds. Soldered construction, twisted wire detail, 1⅛ x 1¾", 3.2 gm. DS
137. Nose ornament, two grotesque animal heads, three conical bosses between. Soldered construction, wire and gold bead detail, 1¼ x 1⅝ x ¾", 7 gm. DS
     (Compare motif with gold bowl # 142-B)
138. Repoussé cylinder with bird finial, pendant from beak, turquoise bead eyes. Soldered construction, 2⅛" h., 5.15 gm. DS
139. Feline head with circular dangles on ears and brow. Belt or headdress ornament. Frias. 4½ x 5½", 92 gm. MBL

VIRU PHASE (?) REPOUSSÉ GOLD

140. Five repoussé gold nose ornaments imitating Mature Phase motifs. DS
    - A. Crescent with large and small conical bosses, $1\frac{3}{8}$ x $2\frac{3}{4}$", 3.1 gm. (Compare with # 133-F.)
    - B. Pierced work, rampant condors, $1\frac{7}{8}$ x $2\frac{3}{4}$", 10.1 gm. (Compare with # 104.)
    - C. Repoussé cat face, $3\frac{3}{4}$ x $3\frac{7}{8}$", 23.9 gm.
    - D. Repoussé cat face, eyes were inlaid, $1\frac{3}{4}$ x $2\frac{5}{8}$", 5.8 gm.
    - E. Half round, rampant repoussé feline and 9 round dangles in cutout holes, 3 x $3\frac{1}{8}$", 7.4 gm.

141. Six repoussé nose ornaments in Viru style tradition. DS
    - A. Three birds and two felines, $3\frac{1}{4}$ x 4", 16.2 gm.
    - B. Grotesque face, $3\frac{1}{2}$ x $4\frac{5}{8}$", 11.5 gm.
    - C. Frontal face with scroll, $2\frac{3}{4}$ x $3\frac{1}{2}$", 7.5 gm.
    - D. Rampant felines, $3\frac{3}{8}$ x 4", 12.4 gm.
    - E. Rampant "dragons", 3x4", 10 gm. (Compare with painted motif on # 128.)
    - F. Double-headed centipede, 2 x $2\frac{1}{2}$", 4.25 gm.

142. Two repoussé gold bowls. DS
    - A. Four frontal faces, $3\frac{1}{8}$ x $5\frac{7}{8}$", 82.1 gm.
    - B. Scroll repeat of grotesque heads, $2\frac{3}{4}$ x $4\frac{3}{8}$", 43 gm. (Compare motif with # 137.)

CLASSIC VICUS COPPER ARTIFACTS, 400 B.C.–100 A.D.

143. Seven ceremonial axe heads, listed according to modeled decoration on socket. DS
   - A. Chavinoid head. Gilded copper, turquoise inlays in eyes and ears, 4 1/8″ long. Chavinoid Phase.
   - B. Three ribs (see stone mace # 148 B). Gilded copper, 4 1/8″ h. Chavinoid Phase.
   - C. Head of warrior. Copper, stone inlaid eyes, 4″ long. Chavinoid Phase (?)
   - D. Figure of seated warrior. Gilded copper, shell inlay in headdress, 3 5/8″ long. Mature Phase (?)
   - E. Head of bat. Copper, turquoise bead eye inlays, 3 7/8″ long. Mature Phase.
   - F. Human head. Copper, 4 1/4″ long. Mature Phase.
   - G. Human head. Silver colored metal (electrum ?), 4 1/8″ long. Viru Phase.

144. Two sculptural mace heads. DS
   - A. Bird form mace, tail making short blade. Gilded copper, 2 1/4 x 3 1/8″. Chavinoid Phase (?)
   - B. Six projecting serpent heads, Copper, 1 1/4″ h. Viru Phase (?)

145. Two flat disc-shaped mace heads. Viru Phase. DS
   (This type also occurs with more typical Classic Vicus motifs.)
   - A. Disc with four notched flanges. Gilded copper, 3 3/4″ diameter.
   - B. Disc with notched rim, seven cutout stylized serpent heads. Gilded copper, 5/8″ h., 5 1/4″ diameter. (Compare with painted motif on # 127.)

146. Celt, pommel in form of owl. Copper, green stone inlays, 3 1/4″ h. Chavinoid Phase (?) DS

147. Small seated figure holding spondylus shell. Copper casting, 2 1/2″ h. Period undetermined. DS

CLASSIC VICUS STONE ARTIFACTS, 400 B.C.–100 A.D.

148. Five mace heads. DS
   - A. Four vertical flanges. Andesite porphyry, 3 3/8″ diameter. Chavinoid Phase.
   - B. Horizontal ribs. Andesite porphyry, 2 1/2″ h. Chavinoid Phase.
   - C. Five rows of square bosses. Stone, 2 1/4″ h. Mature Phase (?)
   - D. Six projecting round knobs. Andesite porphyry, 1 5/8″ h. Mature phase (?)
   - E. Four profile felines in relief. Soapstone, 3 3/8″ h. Viru Phase.

149. Four frontal feline heads. Soapstone, 1″ h. Viru Phase. AC

150. Stone double pipe whistle, feline head pommel, 1 7/8″ h. Viru Phase. ANON

151. Stone double pipe whistle, form of woman carrying olla on back. Basalt, 1 7/8″ h. Mature Phase. DS

152. Small stone cylindrical shaft, seated feline holding human figure on pommel. Function unknown. Type of soapstone, 3 5/8″ h. Mature Phase. DS

153. Eight necklaces of restrung gold and stone beads. Assigned to the Classic Vicus period on the basis of their similarity to Mochica work. DS
   - A. Flattened gold spheres and turquoise, 33 1/2″ long, 160 gm.
   - B. Emeralds and gold, 31″ long.
   - C. Quartz, carnelian, and gold, 30″ long.
   - D. Gold, emerald, topaz, amethyst and other stones, 33″ long.
   - E. Topaz, amethyst, and one emerald, 29 1/2″ long.
   - F. Quartz and gold, 33 1/2″ long.
   - G. Amethyst and gold, 32″ long.
   - H. Pearls, 36″ long.

THE NEGATIVE VICUS STYLE, 100–700 A.D.

In 1966 Dr. Hans Disselhoff conducted a brief excavation at Vicus in which he encountered burials containing negative decorated pottery. Carbon 14 tests of organic materials found associated with them yielded dates averaging around 300 A.D. This important discovery establishes without question the fact that the negative style follows that of the Classic Vicus and is roughly contemporary with the fourth period of Mochica. It does not, however, provide a basis for the chronological ordering of the many stylistic variations within Negative Vicus pottery. The broad period designations proposed here are tentative and need further refinement by careful seriation.

TRANSITIONAL NEGATIVE VICUS CERAMICS, 100–200 A.D.

The earliest ceramics of the Negative Vicus Period clearly show the influence of the Classic Vicus tradition it displaced. Classic subjects are translated into the more primitive negative wares and the stirrup spout form is often copied. Only rarely, however, did the new ceramists use the fine clays preferred by their predecessors.

Orangeware with negative decoration, unless otherwise indicated

154. Fish. Creamware, negative decoration, 8⅝″ h. DS
155. Seated man, necklace of human heads. (Compare with Classic Vicus Viru phase # 119.) 6¾″ h. DS
156. Seated man, hand to face, 7¼″ h. DS
157. Seated woman, braided hair, 6½″ h. DS
158. Seagull, 9¼″ h. ANON
159. Two wrestlers (compare with # 124). The subject and stirrup spout are an imitation of Classic Vicus. The figures are in the Early Negative Vicus style, 11⅜″ h. DS
160. Crescent-shaped bottle, incised double-headed snake, modeled bird. (See # 141 F and # 185.) 8¼″ h. DS

172

THE EARLY NEGATIVE VICUS STYLE, 200–500 A.D.

Ceramics of the Early Negative Vicus period bear some style relationships to those of Viru but are much more primitive and exhibit far less technical skill. Closer stylistic relationships may be found to the north, with pottery found in Ecuador and Columbia. Whatever their cultural ties may have been, Negative Vicus ceramics have a persuasive, almost childlike, charm of their own. The examples listed are, with few exceptions, of two ceramic types. One is a double vessel, one-half bottle, the other, a sculptural figure. The other is a watermellon-shaped bottle with a spout and a bridge-like handle leading to a modeled head or figure. Both types have a whistle in the sculptural portion which sounds when liquid within the ceramic is sloshed.

Orangeware with negative and cream slip decoration

161. Standing male playing drum, 9⅛″ h. DS
162. Standing female, hands held on stomach, 7⅜″ h. DS
163. Standing male, playing pipes of pan, 9¼″ h. DS
*164. Standing female, holding child to front, 7¼″ h. DS
165. Large double-ended drum with handle in the form of anthropomorphic figure, 18⅞ x 12¾″. ANON
166. House form, seated figure inside holding bowl, 7½″ h. DS
167. Bottle, head of man wearing large nose ornament, 8½″ h. AMNH
168. Bottle, head of grotesque bird, 9⅞″ h. DS
169. Bird effigy bottle, condor (?) 8½″ h. DS
170. Bird effigy bottle, long slim neck and body, cream slip only. 10″ h. GG
171. Bird effigy bottle, flaring disc around eye, 7⅞″ h. AMNH
*172. Female effigy, large heart-shaped head, 7½″ h. RA

THE LATE NEGATIVE VICUS STYLE, 500–700 A.D.

In the late period of the Negative Vicus style the same ceramic forms continued but tended to become smaller, better executed, and more elaborate in their negative and cream slip decoration. Spouts become longer and more tapered until at the end of the period the double spout bottle form became a direct precedent for those of the later North Coast Wari, Lambayeque, Chimu, and Inca wares. (# 183.)

173. Effigy bottle, swimmer with arms on skin float, 5⅜″ h. DS
174. Male effigy, standing figure with hands on chest. Heart-shaped head, 11¾″ h. GG
175. Animal effigy bottle, human head, 6″ h. DS
176. Standing deer atop drum shape, 9¼″ h. DS
177. Standing feline atop drum shape, 8¼″ h. DS
178. Monkey atop drum shape, 7½″ h. DS
179. Man held by double-headed animal, 7″ h. DS
180. Rat atop fruit form, 6⅛″ h. DS
181. Rectangular vessel with bottle-shaped spout and seated figure with large nose ornament, 7⅝″ h. DS
*182. Seated monkey, 6⅞″ h. DS
183. Standing figure with flanged headdress, prominent teeth. Wari influence (?), 6½″ h. DS

NEGATIVE VICUS GOLD, 100–500 A.D.

The metalurgical skills of the Negative Vicus peoples were not as advanced as their predecessors'. They did, however, master the technique of combining gold with electrum to form heavy bi-metallic nose ornaments. (# 184) The wearing of this type of ornament is shown in ceramic # 107 where the bi-metallic division is clearly indicated. Ceramic # 181 shows a late period version of the same kind of nose ornament. The dangles of # 184-A may indicate that it belongs in the transition period, but no assignment to period is attempted for the other pieces.

184. Eleven nose ornaments. DS
    - A. Gold half-moon with 5 holes on the points for dangles, 2¾ x 3⅝", 41.2 gm.
    - B. Gold circular piece with two scrolls, 2 x 2¼", 19.1 gm.
    - C. Gold crescent with two beads on wire, 2¾" x 3", 17 gm.
    - D. Gold half-moon with projecting nose pincer, 2 x 4⅛", 19.5 gm.
    - E. Gold squared crescent, 4⅜ x 7", 67.05 gm.
    - F. Gold crescent, band of electrum, 3½ x 4⅞", 59.25 gm.
    - G. Crescent, alternating bands of gold and electrum, 3 x 3⅜", 41.1 gm.
    - H. Gold crescent, harlequin of gold and electrum, 2¾ x 3¼", 49.8 gm.
    - I. Crescent, half gold, half electrum, 2½ x 3⅜", 17.2 gm.
    - J. Half-round, half gold, half electrum, 2½ x 3⅜", 14 gm.
    - L. Gold crescent, 2⅜ x 2⅝", 42 gm.

NEGATIVE VICUS STYLE COPPER OBJECTS

Negative Vicus period copper work appears to have been executed with considerably less skill than that of the Classic Vicus period. Most of the selected objects probably belong to the Transitional period (100–200 A.D.).

185. Disc-shaped mace with incised double-headed serpent. (Compare with # 160.) Gilded copper, ½" h., 4⅜" diameter. DS
186. Plaque with incised fanciful animals. Gilded copper, 9¼" diameter. DS
187. Chopper-like knife with stylized head on handle. Copper, 4⅛" h. DS
188. Celt with abstract form of feline on pommel. Copper, shell, and stone inlays, 6⅜" long. DS
189. Celt with form of feline on pommel. (Compare with # 177.) Copper, 8⅞" long. DS

164 182

NEGATIVE VICUS STYLE STONE

190. Small stone figure, probably from the Late Negative Vicus period. Basalt, 3″ h. EN

THE EARLY HISTORY OF THE NORTH COAST OF PERU

Thanks mainly to the research and publications of Rafael Larco Hoyle, the chronological sequence of ancient cultures on the north coast is well understood. He has shown that a group called Salinar moved into the area at the close of the Cupisnique (Coastal Chavin) period and that it was soon supplanted by the Viru (Gallinazo) culture. The Mochica (Moche) people then occupied the Chicama and Moche Valleys, but the Viru style continued to dominate the nearby Viru Valley. We have already witnessed the impact of the Viru culture on the late phase of Classic Vicus art on the far north coast. The ceramics listed below demonstrate the inter-mixing of styles which took place in the transition period between Chavin and Mochica times, and the Viru style, in the valley for which it is named.

200

THE MINGLING OF STYLES, 400-200 B.C.
CHAVIN - SALINAR - VIRU

191. Bottle form of frog. Cream ware with red-orange slip decoration, $7\frac{7}{8}$" h. MNA
The stirrup spout form is strongly Chavinoid, the technology is Salinar.
192. Bottle in form of seated man. Creamware, incised lines and orange slip. (Style mixture similar to # 191.) $6\frac{3}{4}$" h. SD
Headdress form is also found in Chavinoid phase of Classic Vicus.
193. Cup, owl head. Orangeware, $3\frac{3}{4}$" h. Salinar. SD
194. Bottle in form of parrot. Buff ware, red and cream slip, $5\frac{7}{8}$" h. Salinar, Viru influence. GG
195. Bottle, man lying on mat. Cream ware with orange slip, $4\frac{7}{8}$" h. Salinar style with Viru influenced spout and handle. ANON
196. Bottle, kneeling warrior. Orangeware, Mochica I type stirrup spout, $8\frac{3}{4}$" h. SD

THE VIRU CERAMIC STYLE, 300 B.C.-100 A.D.

Items are arranged in chronological order. Unless otherwise noted, they have typical Viru tapered spouts and arched tubular handles.

197. Bird effigy. Creamware, red slip on eye, nose only, $4\frac{1}{8}$" h. Salinar influence. MAT
198. Man seated atop muffin-shaped bottle. Creamware, traces of red slip, $6\frac{1}{8}$" h. Salinar influence. MAT
199. Bowl, orangeware, negative decoration, $1\frac{3}{4}$" h., 6" diameter. MAT
*200. Double vessel, one-half bottle form; other house form with 4 human heads. Orangeware, negative decoration, $6\frac{1}{8}$" h. GG
201. Crescent form bottle. Warrior head and arms one end. Orangeware, negative decoration, $7\frac{7}{8}$" h. ML
202. Bowl on stand. Human face in relief. Orangeware, traces of cream slip, $5\frac{7}{8}$" h. GG
203. Standing male effigy bottle, spout at back. Orangeware, $16\frac{5}{8}$" h. ML
204. Feline figure. Orangeware, negative decoration, 7" h. GG
205. Feline figure. Orangeware, $8\frac{7}{8}$" h. ML
206. Seated man. Orangeware, $8\frac{3}{4}$" h. MBL
207. Figure playing drum made of human skin. Creamware, orange slip, $7\frac{1}{2}$" h. ANON
208. Effigy bottle, standing figure holding bowl to front. Orangeware, cream slip, $7\frac{3}{4}$" h. Santa Valley. AMNH

THE RECUAY CULTURE, 300 B.C.–700 A.D.

Another culture which exerted a formative influence on the early phases of the Mochica style was Recuay, named after a town in the highland valley called the Callijon de Huaylas where its ceramics were first found. The Recuay style is encountered over an extremely wide area, including the coastal valleys from the Viru to the Casma and inland to the Marañon. Its center appears to have been the Santa river drainage (which includes the Callijon) but little is known of its history and stylistic development.

216 221 (above) 222

THE RECUAY CERAMIC STYLE, 300 B.C.-700 A.D.

The following Recuay ceramics are creamwares strikingly decorated with negative painted designs and orange slip, unless otherwise noted. The sculptural forms are simplified and highly stylized. Pieces are arranged in what may be their approximate chronological order without indicating periods.

209. Bottle with Chavinoid stirrup spout. Band of spider motifs, animal figures above, 7½" h. Viru Valley (?) WG
210. Effigy bottle. Cream ware with red and orange slip, negative black, zone decoration, 6¾" h. ANON
211. Bowl, serpents in relief. 2½" h., 4⅞" diameter. RA
212. Three spoons. RA
    A. Bird pommel, 5" h.
    B. Two animal head pommel, 5½" h.
    C. Animal head pommel, 5¼" h.
213. Pair, figures holding jars to front. Orangeware, cream slip and negative decoration. Viru Valley. RA
    A. 6⅝" h.
    B. 6⅝" h.
214. Seated figure, surrounded by seven smaller figures on top of vessel. All hold cups. 8¼" h. DS
215. Seated warrior (one leg missing). 10" h. Marañon Valley. MNA

*216. Standing warrior with elaborate owl mask headdress, llama at his side, 13½" h. ANON

217. Llama with condor seated on head, 4½" h. MA
218. Effigy bottle, panels of serpent motifs, 8⅜" h. ANON
219. Blackware effigy bottle, 5" h. ANON
220. Flanged bottle, human head and two house forms on top, 7⅞" h. DS

*221. Elaborate house form, seated warrior on flat roof with four smaller figures holding cups, three similar figures on floor below. Negative panels on alternating orange and white ground, 10¾" h. FT

*222. Deer effigy bottle. Thin orangeware, white slip and negative décor, 8¼" h. DS

223. Effigy jar, vertical flanges at sides. Orangeware, cream slip and negative décor, 10½" h. MAT
224. Feline effigy jar, 6⅛" h. JP
225. Flaring rim effigy bottle, clams on side, modeled heads. 6⅝" h. GG
226. Seated figure holding knife and trophy head (feline teeth not Chavin but Wari influence), 8⅞" h. MNA
227. Seated figure. Headdress, orange slip on cream face, black negative on orange. 8⅜" h. ANON
228. Bowl, creamware, negative décor exterior, orange slip interior. 3⅝" h. RA Transitional with Cjamarca style.
229. Effigy jar. Seated man playing flute. Orangeware, black and mauve slip. ANON

RECUAY STONE SCULPTURE, 300 B.C.-700 A.D.

The highland stone temples of the Recuay culture were ornamented with sculptured tenoned heads, high reliefs, and free-standing figure sculpture. In Post-Wari times, this practice continued, though the carvings are more primitive. The late style is called Huaylas. The dividing line between the two styles is difficult to define.

230. Tenoned head, square snouted plumed puma (plumes in serpent form). Rhyolite porphyry, 10x8¾x18¾". Pallasca, a site in the upper northern reaches of the Santa Valley drainage. ML
231. Pair, felines in high relief within arched borders. Rhyolite porphyry. Callijon de Huaylas. MNA
    A. Facing right, 16x20½x7½".
    B. Facing left, 16x20½x10½".
232. Seated warrior, holding broad necklace with pendant trophy head. Rhyolite porphyry, 20¼" h. MM

THE MOCHICA CULTURE, 200 B.C.-700 A.D.

Mochica ceramics are perhaps the best known art of ancient Peru. The sensitive realism of their modeled subjects and the animation and expressiveness of their painted scenes have often been noted. The superlative examples shown in this exhibition can only enhance the style's reputation as one of the greatest ceramic traditions the world has ever seen.

Rafael Larco published detailed studies of the Mochica ceramic style in which he defined five periods. The first three appear to have been rather short evolutionary phases, while the fourth was a long period of maturity and the fifth a period of gradual decline. With the discovery of the Classic Vicus style, it became apparent that the origin of the Mochica culture could not be explained in terms of developments in the Chicama and Moche Valleys alone. It must have been strongly influenced by its northern counterpart, and did not assume artistic leadership of the joint tradition until its third period.

All Mochica ceramics listed are stirrup spout bottles unless otherwise indicated

THE MOCHICA I CERAMIC STYLE, 200-50 B.C.

Ceramics of this period were simple and monumental with little of the attention to detail which characterized the Mature Classic Vicus style (compare Nos. 108 and 236).

Stirrup spout bottles with thickened spout lips as in classic vicus ceramics

233. Band of red and cream scroll motifs. Orangeware, 6" h. MNA
234. Painted octopus. Red, cream slip ground, 6⅞" h. MAT
235. Architectural complex. Red, orange ground, 7⅝" h. MNA
236. Frog. Orangeware, red slip spots, 4⅞" h. MNA

*237. Llama with saddle bags. Red, cream slip ground, 7⅛" h. GG

237

THE MOCHICA II CERAMIC STYLE, 50–0 B.C.

The trend towards realism continues. Ceramics were mold made. Spout lips are slightly thickened. The period was short and Nos. 139 and 141 are transistional to period III.

238. Relief of Recuay type feline heads. Blackware, 9¼" h. MA
239. Seated woman, child at side with box drum (?). Dark grey-ware, 6"h. MNA

*240. Seated bound prisoner. Traces of cream and black, brown ground, 9⅜" h. SD

241. Painted lizzards and algarobo beans. Cream, red ground, 6½" h. GG
242. Seated man, foot amputated, forehead ornament missing. Cream and red, orange ground, 11¾" h. ML
243. Head with bird on top. Original from which mold sections were made. Orangeware, 7½" h. DS
244. Mochica god Ai Apec holding knife and trophy head. (Spout replaced.) (Compare with Classic Vicus # 102.) Red, cream ground, 9¾" h. FT

240

THE MOCHICA III CERAMIC STYLE, 0-200 A.D.

In the third period Mochica ceramic art reached technical and artistic maturity. The cameo-like perfection of its finest wares was never to be surpassed. A greater range of colored slips were employed. Spouts had a characteristic flaring rim and were sometimes concave in profile.

MOCHICA III PAINTED AND RELIEF WARES

*245. Bottle, half red on cream, half cream on red, painted concentric circles, 7⅛″ h. RA
246. Abstract bird motifs. Red, white ground, 7¾″ h. GG
247. Chavinoid, broad line incised bird. Cream incisions on orange ground, 9″ h. MAT
248. Chavinoid, broad line incised feline mask, punctated background. Band of fish demons. Red incisions on orange ground. Band of fish, red on cream, 8½″ h. MNA
249. Low ovoid form with 5 round bosses. Deep orange with lighter orange spout, 8″ h. EN

MOCHICA III MODELED WARES

Orangeware with cream slip unless otherwise indicated

*250. Seated man, incised face markings, striped shirt. 5½″ h. MAT
*251. Duck, incised wing detail. 5″ h. ML
252. Man and woman making corn beer ("Chicha"). 4⅞″ h. MBL
253. Standing woman holding bowl (no spout). 9⅛″ h. SD
254. Jar, Owl holding mouse in beak. 12⅞″ h. GG
255. Jar, Warrior holding drum. 16⅛″ h. SD
256. Ocelot. 8⅞″ h. MNA
257. Seated man, large ear ornaments (see No. 301). 9½″ h. SD
258. Portrait head. 11″ h. WG
259. Seated man, beans painted in black on face. 11″ h. WG
260. Kneeling warrior (headdress restored). 9½″ h. GG

MOCHICA III BLACKWARES

Highly polished black wares were made in all Mochica periods but they enjoyed their greatest popularity in Period III. The examples below were selected for comparison with Nos. 256–260. Because of their confusion with Chimu black wares, missing blackware spouts were sometimes replaced with spouts of that later period (Nos. 263, 265).

261. Feline. 8¼″ h. SD
262. Seated warrior, incised detail, some shell inlays intact. Spout missing. (Early Period IV). 10½″ h. MNA
263. Portrait head, spout replaced. 10¾″ h. SD
264. Seated grotesque figure. 9½″ h. MNA
265. Standing warrior, owl mask. Spout replaced. 10″ h. (headdress missing). SD

245 251 250

282

THE MOCHICA IV CERAMIC STYLE, 200-500 A.D.

During the fourth period, the Mochica extended their domain northward to the Jequetepeque Valley and southward to the Napeña welding over 200 miles of the North Coast into a vigorous political and social unit. The terms, early, middle, and late are used to indicate the portion of the long period to which ceramics belong.

MOCHICA IV PAINTED WARES

Red on cream slip ground

266. Diamond-shaped abstract heads (Early). 10½″ h. MNA
267. Battle scene (Early). 9⅛″ h. ANON
268. Deer hunt (Early). Red on cream ground, 11½″ h. AICG
269. Bowl, combat of sea demons (Early). 7⅞″ h., 15″ diameter. MAT
270. Snail gatherers in the mountains (Middle). 10⅜″ h. MNA
271. Offering of conch shells to chieftain (Middle). 11⅜″ h. ML
272. Procession of warriors and military ritual scenes (Late). 21⅛″ h. ML
273. Deer hunt (Late – transition to Period V). 12½″ h. MNA

MOCHICA IV MODELED WARES

274. Jar, four demon faces in relief (Early). Blackware, 13½″ h. ES
275. Jar. Bird form (Early). Orangeware, cream paint, 13¾″ h. ML
276. Pair jars, bound prisoners (Middle). Red and cream, 13¼″ h. GG
277. Kneeling drummer (Middle). Cream and orange, 11¾″ h. GG
278. Portrait jar, open mouth, (Early). Cream and orange, 7″ h. MNA
279. Portrait jar, tatooed lip (Early). Cream, light orange, red, 8″ h. ML
280. Portrait, 2 bird-skin headdress (Middle). Brown and cream, 12½″ h. ML
281. Portrait, one-eyed personage (Middle). Red and cream, 11⅜″ h. AICG

*282. Portrait, fat man (Late). Orange with red lines, 11⅜″ h. MA

283. Figure, seated blind man, hand to mouth (Early). Cream, orange, and red, 10¼″ h. MNA
284. Head, blind man, arms painted on vessel (Middle). Orange, cream and red, 10¼″ h. ANON
285. Head of dignitary, arms painted on vessel (Middle). Orange, cream and red, 10½″ h. MNA
286. Anthropomorphic peanut (Man playing flute) (Early). Orange, cream, and deep red, 8½″ h. TG
287. Man with pouches under eyes (Early). Orange, 9⅜″ h. GG
288. Fox (spout missing) (Middle). Red and cream, 6⅝″ h. RA
289. Two fox cubs playing (Middle). Orange, red, and cream, 6⅝″ h. RA
290. Seagull, (Middle). Brown and cream, 7¾″ h. FT
291. Seated monkey (Late). Orange and cream, 8¾″ h. MBL
292. Seated bat god (compare with Classic Vicus version # 87). (Early). Orange and cream, 8¼″ h. MNA

THE MOCHICA V CERAMIC STYLE, 500–700 A.D.

The last period of the Mochica culture was one of gradual decline as it experienced the ever increasing pressure of the agressive highland Wari people which finally brought about its collapse around 700 A.D. Both modeled and painted pottery were often executed in a rather perfunctory manner. Painted ceramics in particular express a kind of nervous tension which must have been characteristic of the times. The surfaces of vessels were crowded with motifs and space fillers.
Number 294 of this exhibition is a most extraordinary masterpiece of the Mochica V period. Literally hundreds of animated figures are crowded upon the bottles' surface, acting out an elaborate ritual scene evidently representing offerings being brought to the warrior king. It is as if by their intensity they sought to stave off their impending doom. The work is an eloquent testimony of the tenacious vitality of a long and glorious tradition.

MOCHICA V CERAMICS

293. Painted, ritual scene above, warriors in combat below. Centipedes on stirrup and spout. Cream and orange, 11½″ h. MNA
*294. Painted, elaborate ritual scene, offerings to the king. Cream and orange, 11⅛″ h. GG
295. Painted, harlequin fashion. Ai Apec crab demon. Cream and brown, 7″ h. RA
296. Bivalve shell fish. Cream and brown, 8″ h. SD
297. Abstract head of eagle demon. Cream and brown, 9⅛″ h. MAT
298. Head jar, anthropomorphic condor. Cream and orange, 9⅞″ h. MBL
299. Portrait jar. Cream and orange, 5″ h. Batan Grande, Lambayeque Valley. HZ

MOCHICA GOLD

300. Pectoral, human face with vestigial body, flanked by sky pumas. 11 x 11½″. III Purpur, Viru Valley. ML
*301. Pair ear spools, stone and shell inlays and 8 radiating lizzard forms. 3⅜″ h., 3″ diameter. III Purpur, Viru Valley. ML
302. Plain gold bowl. 2¾″ h., 5⅝″ diameter, 90.1 gm. III. EC
303. Frog (?) Soldered construction. 2¼″ h., 37 gm. III. GG
304. Necklace, 9 ears of corn, 9 flattened ovoid beads with relief of warrior killing fox. 36″ long. IV. EC
305. Single bead from necklace similar to # 304, composite deity symbol. Human face and two profile puma heads. 3½″ h., 5″ diameter, 77.2 gm. IV. GG
306. Pectoral or headdress ornament, relief of elaborately dressed personage playing pipes of pan, flanked by trumpeters. 10½ x 13½″. IV. GG
307. Plaque, 2 priest figures. 3½″ x 4¼″, 18.8 gm. V. TMDC

MISCELLANEOUS MOCHICA ART

*308. Silver head jar of Ai Apec with gold overlaid on teeth and eyes of serpent head ear ornaments, green stone eye inlays. IV. 6⅜″ h. IV. TG
*309. Copper face mask. 7⅞″ h. V. MBL
310. Stone head cup, gold and turquoise eyes, gold clamps. 2½″ h. III. HC
311. Ceremonial wooden digging stick, male figure on pommel, inlays. 72″ long. III. MNA
312. Ceremonial wooden digging stick, jaguar crouching on corpse pommel. 54″ long, pommel 7″. IV. ANON
313. Wooden lime bottle in the form of a seated prisoner, bound with serpent cord. 4¼″ h. IV. ML

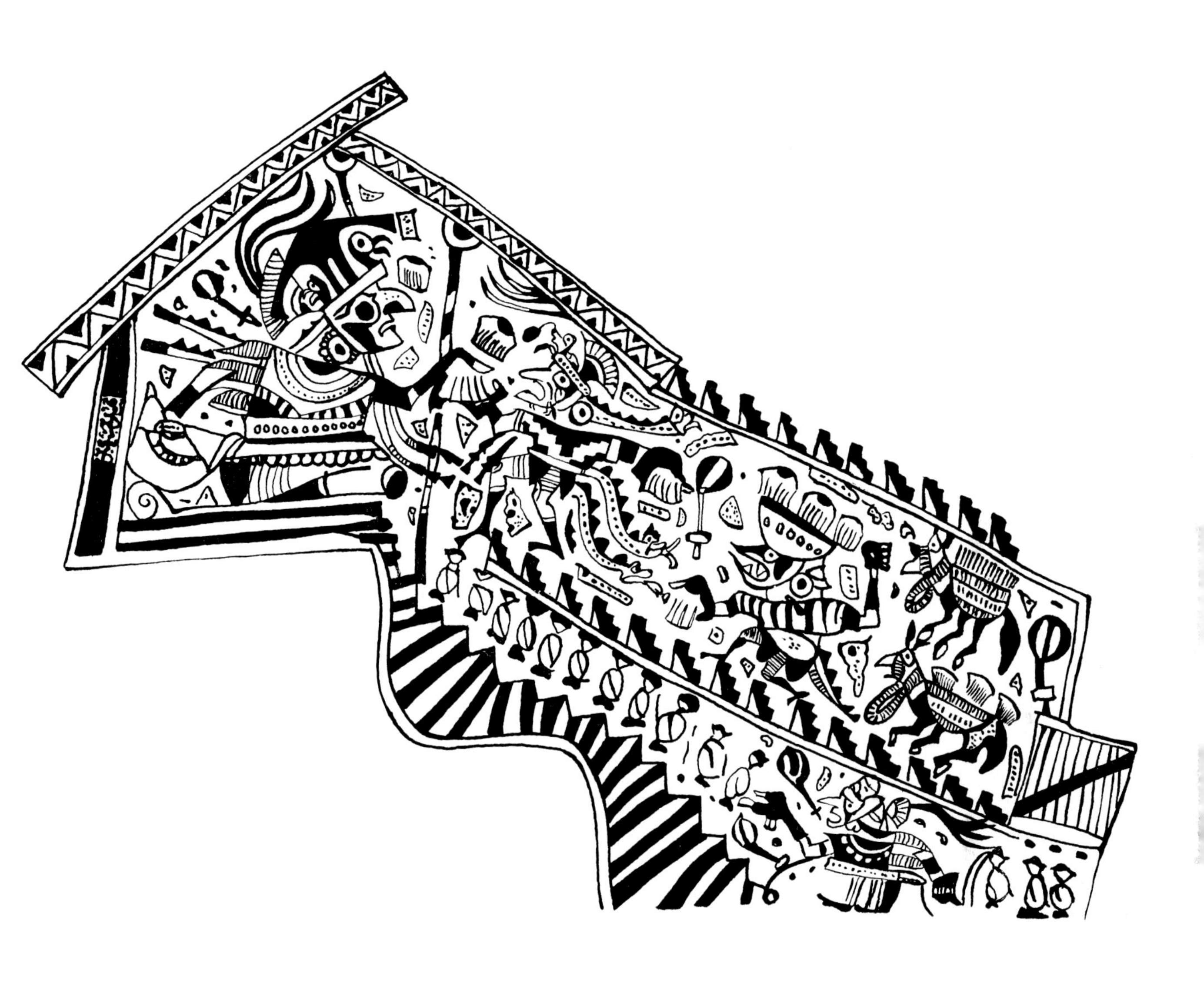

Detail from catalogue no. 294 (illustrated opposite)

301

308

THE PARACAS CULTURE, 1,100-200 B.C.

The term Paracas is used to cover a very long and complex interplay of cultural traditions that took place on the south coast of Peru during most of the first millennium B.C. Archeological information is spotty and chronological relationships between regional styles as well as dating are a matter of some speculation. The general trends of cultural development are known, however, and the periods indicated place objects in their relative positions in time. Numbered phase designations published by Menzel, Rowe and Dawson are correlated with these periods on the chronology chart. Like Tembladera ceramics, those of Paracas styles generally have well preserved paints applied after firing. Potteries have incised designs and the typical form is a double spout bottle with one spout non-functional and in the form of a modeled head. Exceptions are noted.

309

CHAVINOID PARACAS CERAMICS, 1,100-700 B.C.

The Paracas culture began with a period of strong Chavin influence during which changing stylistic trends in the north were reflected. The first two examples are negative wares which may represent the local pre-Chavin pottery tradition. They are curiously related to early Columbian and Ecuadorian ceramic styles.

314. Double spout bottle, loop handle between. Orange ware, negative decoration. 8¾″ h. Excavated at Paracas by Engel. IAA
315. Cup. Orangeware, negative decoration. 4⅝″ h. Excavated at Paracas by Engel. IAA
316. Stirrup spout bottle with feline mask, incised guilloche on sides. Published by Tello as Chavin. Brown, 6½″ h. Provenience unknown, though similar bottles have been found at Callango, Ica Valley. MNA
317. Bowl with modelled monkey on side and rim. (Similar to a north highland type found at Pacopampa.) Blackware, orange and brown paint, 3½″ h. Huayuri, Santa Cruz Valley. HA
318. Double spout whistle bottle, feline mask to front. Blackware, red, yellow and brown paint, 6¼″ high. Chiquerillo, Ica Valley. ANON
319. Bowl, band of Chavin eye and teeth motifs. Blackware, red and cream paint, 2¼″ h., 4¼″ diameter. Ocucaje. TMDC
320. Double spout whistle bottle. Chavinoid face to front. Blackware, red and brown paint, 7⅛″ h. Ocucaje, Ica Valley. PT
321. Bowl, fox (?) and vencejo (bird) motifs. Blackware, red and brown paint, 3⅜″ h. Ocucaje. MNA
322. Double spout whistle bottle. Chavinoid feline mask. Blackware, red, brown and tan paint, 7½″ h. Ocucaje. PT
323. Pitcher, double-headed serpent motif. Blackware, yellow, brown and green paint, 5⅜″ h. Ocucaje. PT
*324. Single spout bottle, modeled feline. Blackware, cream, red and tan paint, 7⅞″ h. Callango, Ica Valley. CS
325. Double spout bottle, one spout blind in form of human head. Bowl base with two human and one feline Chavinoid faces. Tanware, white, green and orange paint, 7″ h. Callango. ANON
326. Bowl, Chavinoid faces. Blackware, red and cream paint, 3⅜″ h. Callango. ANON

EARLY PARACAS CERAMICS, 700–500 B.C.

By 700 B.C. distinctive regional Paracas styles had developed which continued more or less independent from Late Chavin style trends in the north. Sites are indicated on the accompanying map.

327. Human head spout, bowl base with geometric décor. Blackware, traces of red, 6⅛″ h. Juan Pablo. PT
328. Bird head spout, feline mask. Blackware, traces of red, 6⅞″ h. Juan Pablo. PT
329. Bird head spout, two panels of vencejo (bird) motifs on negative spotted ground. Blackware, yellow and orange paint, 5½″ h. Juan Pablo. PT
330. Pair. Bird head spouts, feline masks with border of geometric decor. Juan Pablo. TMDC
*331. Bird head spout, feline mask and fox figures. Maize, red-brown, black and dark brown, 5½″ h., 6⅛″ diameter. Spouts restored. Excavated at Paracas by Engel. IAA
332. Modeled feline. Blackware, ochre, red and green paint, 7″ h. Ocucaje. PT
333. Two open spouts, feline figure on each side. Blackware, traces of red and brown paint, 4⅜″ h. Ocucaje. DS
334. Falcon head spout, wings and body below. Blackware, red and yellow paint, 7⅛″ h. Callango. DS
335. Human head spout. Blackware, orange paint, red and grey in incisions, 10⅞″ h. Callango. GS
336. Effigy bottle. Blackware, red and cream paint, 6⅛″ h. Callango. GS
337. Effigy bottle. Blackware, red and cream paint, 6⅛″ h. Callango. GS
338. Negative decorated football-shaped bottle. Blackware, red, yellow and brown paint, 5⅞″ h. Callango. GS
339. Bowl, birds and felines. Blackware, red and yellow paint, 2¾″ h., 8¾″ diameter. Callango. DS

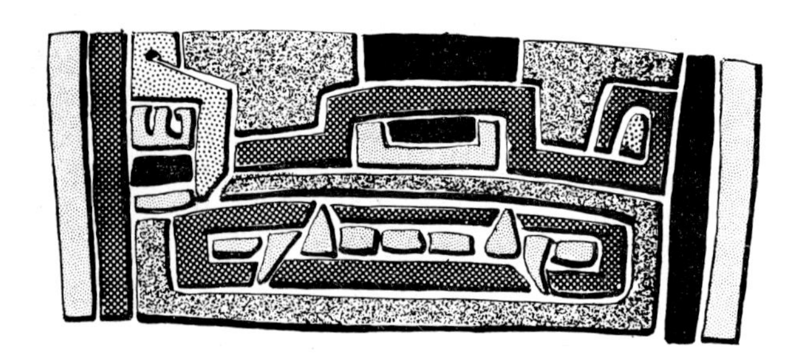

MIDDLE PARACAS CERAMICS, 500–300 B.C.

Around 500 B.C. a new religion and iconography involving a trophy head cult gained dominance at Ocucaje and other important centers while it appears to have had relatively less effect on others that continued to follow their Chavinoid traditions. (Juan Pablo, Callango, Palpa Valley.)

340. Large jar with typical trophy head cult motif. The zig-zag expressionistic line of the new style contrasted sharply with the orderly Early Paracas renderings. Orangeware, negative decoration, 17⅝″ h. Ocucaje. AR
341. Cat head spout, body incised. 7″ h. Excavated at Paracas by Tello. MNA
342. Modeled fish, killer whale (?) Excavated at Paracas by Engel. Blackware, yellow and red paint, 3⅜″ h. IAA
*343. Human head spout, winged figure incised. Blackware, yellow, red, brown and green paint, 6¾″ h. Ocucaje. PT
344. Pair bowls, human and feline figures in interior and on base. Callango. GS
    A. Human figure in interior. Red, tan, cream and traces of blue paint, 1¾″ h., 4⅞″ diameter.
    B. Feline figure in interior. Red, tan, cream and traces of blue paint, 1¾″ h., 4⅞″ diameter.
345. Cup, abstract feline figures. Cream, blue and red paint, 5¼″ h. Callango. GS
346. Two head spouts open at top, monkeys incised on sides. Red, green, cream, blue and tan paint, 6⅛″ h. Callango. GS
347. Bowl, felines on interior, fret design. Blackware, red, yellow and green paint, 1¾″ h., 6¼″ diameter. Palpa Valley. MRI
348. Monkey effigy. Blackware, yellow and red paint, 7⅛″ h. Palpa Valley. ANON
349. Falcon head, body and wings incised. Blackware, red, yellow and green paint, 4⅜″ h. Palpa Valley. ANON

LATE PARACAS CERAMICS, 300–200 B.C.

In the late period Paracas ceramics became more elegant in form and line. Subject matter shifted emphasis towards more natural motifs.

350. Large head jar. Blackware, traces of cream and blue paint, 17⅜″ h. Ocucaje. AR
351. Constricted rim jar, falcons. Yellow ground, blue, red-brown and cream paint, 4¾″. Ocucaje. PT
352. Bowl, abstract serpent. Yellow ground, red and olive paint, 2″ h., 6¾″ diameter. Ocucaje. FT
353. Effigy jar. Blackware, dark and pale green, red, orange and brown paint, 9⅛″ h. (Excavated by Duncan Strong.) Ocucaje. MRI
354. Pair three-headed frogs. Ocucaje. PT
    A. Blackware, red, brown and green paint, 5⅝″ long.
    B. Blackware, red, brown and tan paint, 5½″ long.
355. Miniature double spout bottle, killer whales. Blackware, tan, green and red paint, 4⅝″ h. Excavated by Sawyer, Cordero Alto, Ica Valley. MRI
356. Miniature bird effigy bottle. Blackware, traces of red paint, 2⅛″ h. Ocucaje. AR

357. Whistle in form of seated monkey. Blackware, red and yellow paint, 2⅞″ h. Ocucaje. AR

358. Bowl, monkeys. Blackware, cream, orange, light and dark green paint, 3¼″ h. Ocucaje. CS

359. Bowl, 4 human figures, bird. Blackware, red, yellow, cream, green and maroon paint, 6⅝″ h. Ocucaje. AR

360. Bowl, long-necked bird. Blackware, cream, red and green paint, 3″ h., 5⅛″ diameter. Ocucaje. MRI

361. Effigy bottle, seated figure. Blackware, tan, red and white paint, 6″ h. Ocucaje. PT

362. Standing figure, whistle in head band. Blackware, cream and red paint, 11⅛″ h. Ocucaje. AR

363. Standing figure, lock of human hair. Brownware, cream paint on face, 13¼″ h. Ocucaje. ANON

324 331 *(below)* 343 *(above)*

366

PARACAS TEXTILES, 500–200 B.C.

The most famous event in the history of Peruvian art and archeology was unquestionably the discovery of the Paracas Necropolis cemetery by Tello in 1925. On the sandy slopes of a hill called Cerro Colorado overlooking the Paracas bay, he found several hundred funeral bundles within the foundation of ancient buildings. When he opened the larger of these bundles, he found the body encased by layer after layer of exquisitely embroidered mantles and other garments separated by plain cotton shrouds. We are privileged to have a number of these fabulous textiles in this exhibition. Paracas textiles have also been found at Ocucaje and other sites but none match the splendor of the Necropolis fabrics. Most date from the Middle and Late Paracas periods but the most glorious of the Necropolis are now assigned to the following Proto Nazca period. Few have so far been recovered that may be attributed to the Early Paracas and Chavinoid periods.

MIDDLE PARACAS TEXTILES, 500–300 B.C.

364. Funerary mask. Painted, 9¾ x 9¾″ plus 13″ (uneven warps). Ocucaje. CS
365. Poncho. Interlocking snake motif in warp and weft interlock technique. Guilloche border of triple-cloth. 6′ 9⅞″ x 3′ 3¼″. Ocucaje. TMDC
    (Stylistically related to Tello's Pre-Necropolis, "Cavernas" culture at Paracas.)

LATE PARACAS TEXTILES, 300–200 B.C.

*366. Poncho. Eight feline and human figures with serpent streamers. Double cloth. 5′ 11¼″ x 2′ 10¼″. Paracas Necropolis. MNA
367. Gauze panel. Geometric figures similar to # 366. 5′ 11″ x 2′ 5⅛″. Ocucaje. PT
368. Mantle section (?) Four geometricized figures. Double cloth, 5′ 1¾″ x 9½″. Ocucaje. TMDC
369. Mantle, border and bands of geometric feline motifs. Embroidery. 6′ 3″ x 3′ 3″. Paracas Necropolis. MNA
370. Funerary mask. Frontal figure with serpent streamers. Painted. 2′ 9″ x 1′ 4″. Ocucaje. AR
371. Funerary mask. Similar motif, 10¼″ plus 1′ 2⅛″ x 11⅜″. PT
372. Funerary mask. Similar motif, 9⅜″ plus 2′ 6″ x 1′ 1¾″. CS

PARACAS NECROPOLIS, PROTO NAZCA PERIOD,

TEXTILES, 200–100 B.C.

*373. Mantle. Embroidered border of mythical figures. Stepped multi-colored field in interlocking warp and weft technique. 8′ 2¾″ x 3′ 7¼″ (incl. fringe). MNA
374. Mantle, winged figures. 8′ 10″ x 4′ 9¼″ (incl. fringe). MNA
375. Mantle border fragment. 10″ x 4¾″. WG
376. Poncho, cats with birds. 1′ 7⅛″ x 1′ 2″. MNA
*377. Poncho, falcons. 1′ 7⅛″ x 1′ 2″. (Compare with ceramic # 388.) MNA

373

THE PROTO NAZCA PERIOD, 200–100 B.C.

Towards the end of the Late period, Paracas ceramics and textiles began to reflect new religious concepts. An increasing number of natural motifs such as birds and animals joined the symbols of the trophy head cult. In the Proto Nazca period that followed, this trend culminated in the formation of the Nazca culture whose main religious preoccupation was agricultural fertility. At the same time, ceramics were undergoing a technological revolution evidently stimulated by Necropolis techniques but centered in the Rio Grande de Nazca Valley.

NECROPOLIS CERAMIC TYPES, 200–100 B.C.

Necropolis ceramics justly famous for their superb technology and sophisticated simplicity were found by Tello with Proto Nazca period textiles at Cerro Colorado. (Nos. 378–381.) Similar types have been found at Ocucaje (Nos. 382–384).

378. "Grater" bowl with deeply incised fish motif against punctated ground. Tanware, traces of red paint on rim, 2⅞" h., 9½" diameter. MNA
379. Shallow bowl, polished black interior with finely incised fish. 1⅝" h., 8⅞" diameter. MNA
380. Double spout bottle, capped gadrooned form. Orange, 5⅝" h. MNA
381. Single spout bottle in form of frog. White, 4⅞" h. MNA
382. Shallow bowl, black interior with incised fish motif. 2⅞" h., 9" diameter. AR
383. Double spout bottle, capped gadrooned form. Cream, 5⅜" h. AR
384. Double spout bottle, slightly gadrooned form, four frogs in high relief. Orange, 6½" h. AR

377

PROTO NAZCA CERAMICS, 200–100 B.C.

Ceramists shifted from the use of resin paints to colored clay slips as the medium of decorating pottery. At the close of the period ceramics had only to lose their incised lines to become Early Nazca in style.

All examples selected are from Ocucaje.

385. Necropolis type bottle with two ocelots in relief across top. Cream, red spots, 5¼″ h. AR
386. Dog effigy bottle. Cream, orange and black, 7″ h. CS
387. Effigy bottle, fisherman. Cream, red and black, 6¼″ h. CS
*388. Falcon seated on draw-string bag. (Compare with textile # 377). Polychrome, 9⅞″ h. AR
389. Draw-string bag. Red, black and cream, 7⅝″ h. AR
390. Miniature trophy head. Polychrome, 4″ h. AR
391. Double vessels, each with modeled head, incised and slip painted body. Polychrome red ware, 15¾″ h., 28½″ long. AR

388

OTHER PROTO NAZCA ART FORMS, 200–100 B.C.

392. Fan, two condor motifs woven in black and yellow against red ground on structure of canes. Yellow feather fringe, handle missing. CS
393. Gold forehead ornament. 6″ h. x 19¼″ long. AR
394. Bone falcon form, throwing stick handle, 3¼″ long. AR
395. Wooden wolf form with inset pyrites mirror. 2⅛″ h. x 4¼″ long. AR
396. Obsidian knife blade. 4⅜″ long. FS
*397. Stone vase, incised with two elaborate whiskered deities, one holds gold forehead ornament; the other gold plume. Porphyry, 10⅜″ h. MNA

417 411 415

THE EARLY NAZCA STYLE, 100 B.C.-200 A.D.

Ceramic, unless otherwise noted

398. Double spout bottle, capped "Necropolis" form, stars. Polychrome, 7⅝" h. MNA
399. Double spout bottle, capped form. Killer whale, beans. Polychrome, 6¼" h. ANON
400. Double spout bottle, bowl based. Polychrome, 8¾" h. MNA
401. Seated figure wearing turban. Polychrome, 8" h. ANON
*402. Trophy head jar, sling on turban. Polychrome, 6⅞" h. PT
*403. Drum. Complex whiskered diety with fox skin headdress. Polychrome, 20½" h. ANON
404. Seated whiskered diety holding pepino (fruit) and Yuca root (vegetable). Single spout bottle. Polychrome, 8½" h. MNA
405. Double spout bottle. Whiskered diety, serpent tresses. Polychrome, 6⅞" h. MNA
406. Large effigy jar, complex whiskered diety. Polychrome, 28⅝" h. HA
407. Pyro engraved gourd. Winged whiskered diety. (Compare with # 410.) Brown with traces of black in incisions, 5¼" h. MRI
408. Painted textile fragment, whiskered diety holding corn stalk and Yuca root. 10¾ x 8¼". TMDC
409. Gold whisker ornament. 10¼ x 10½". TMDC
410. Winged warrior holding trophy head, falcon eye markings. (Compare with # 406.) Polychrome, 11¼" h. CS
*411. Warrior holding club and trophy head, falcon eye markings. Polychrome, 11" h. HA
412. Double headed spout bottle, falcon eye markings. Warrior figures on vessel below. Cactus, llama, spider, etc. Polychrome, black ground, 9⅝" h. CS
413. Figure carrying large jar with head band. Polychrome, red ground, 5⅞" h. ANON
414. Long-necked bird. Grey, white, red, black, 6⅝" h. MNA
*415. Bird. Pink, brown, red, grey, black and white, 7⅜" h. MNA
416. Four peppers. Orange, cream and black, 5" h. LC
*417. Fox. Brown, white, black and tan, 6½" h. MRI
418. Plate, condor. Brown, white, red, 2⅜" h., 8" diameter. MNA
419. Plate, two fish. Red ground, cream, black, white, orange, 2⅝" h., 8½" diameter. MNA
420. Plate, fish. Black, red, white, 2⅜" h., 8" diameter. CS
421. Plate, six fish, heads protruding beyond rim. Interior grey, red, orange, cream, black; exterior, stripes, 3¼" h., 12¼" diameter. MNA
422. Jar, fish. Grey, white, black, red, 5⅝" h. MRI
423. Cup, fish. Polychrome fish, red ground, 5⅜" h. EN
424. Bowl, 4 crayfish, 4 frogs. Red interior; exterior, white, black, orange, grey, red ground, 4⅜" h., 9" diameter. RA
425. Bowl, birds. Red interior; exterior, white, maroon, black, grey, orange, 5" h., 10¼" diameter. RA
426. Double spout bottle. Killer whales and birds, 7⅜" h. HC
427. Pan pipe, vencejos. Black and red, 7⅛" h. MRI
428. Pan pipe, dashed line. Black, red, and white, 8½" h. MNA
429. Pan pipe. Red. FS
430. Whistle, condor. Grey, cream, red, and black, 8⅛" h. ANON
431. Whistle, figure. Andesite porphyry, 3" long. ANON

THE MIDDLE NAZCA STYLE, 200-300 A.D.

Middle Nazca period ceramics are usually refined in form and decorated with great precision. Subject matter tends to be elaborate and at times is highly abstract (# 443) signaling the final break-up of the Early Nazca tradition of simplicity, as religious concepts underwent a radical change.

432. Jar, serpents, spiders in spider webs. Polychrome, red band at top, 8½″ h. MNA
433. Jar, drowning female figures, water background. Polychrome, white ground, 7″ h. RA
434. Cup, whiskered diety, water background. Polychrome, 3¼″ h. ANON
435. Effigy jar, vegetable diety. Polychrome, white ground, 6″ h. CS
436. Figures with digging sticks. Polychrome, 6″ h. MRI
437. Cup. Elaborate agricultural diety. Polychrome, white ground, 4⅜″ h. MNA
438. Jar. Figures with digging sticks. Red-orange, black, cream ground, 5″ h. FS
439. Painted textile, vegetable guardian figures. 2′ 8⅜″x5′ 2⅜″. TMDC
440. Bowl. Whiskered warrior diety. Red interior, exterior, polychrome, red ground, 4″ h., 9⅝″ diameter. MRI

*441. Double spout bottle. Whiskered warrior diety. Polychrome, white ground, 6¾″ h. MRI

442. Beaker. Warrior with darts, sling, throwing stick and birds. Polychrome, black band near bottom, 9¾″ h. RA
443. Bowl. Abstract condor, trophy head in beak. Interior, polychrome; exterior, red, 3⅜″ h., 8¾″ diameter. CS
444. Figure wearing striped garment. Polychrome, 8¾″ h. ANON
445. Trophy head beaker, falcon eye markings. White and red, 5⅛″ h. ANON
446. Pair trophy head beakers, triangle check markings. White and red. RA
    A. 5⅞″ h.
    B. 6⅛″ h.

465 451 441

467 B 469 467 A

THE LATE NAZCA STYLE, 300-600 A.D.

The beginning of the Late Nazca style is marked by a sudden elaboration in the rendering of whiskered diety motifs. Face whiskers, forehead ornaments and plumes proliferate in detail until they almost obscure the basic motif. These elements are rendered in sharp, crisp lines interspersed with barb-like trophy hair symbols, making the surface of ceramics crackle with energy like a Fourth of July sparkler. (Nos. 447–449.) Vegetable guardian dieties are elaborate but still recognizable (# 450).

The reason for this dramatic change in the Nazca art style is still obscure. Some strong outside influence seems to have been involved and the highland Ayacucho area is suspected as its source. Relationships between the highland cultures and the Nazca grew progressively stronger during the period.

447. Double spout bottle. Standing proliferated figure holding serpents in hands. Border of faces. Polychrome, white ground, 7¾″ h. ANON
448. Double spout bottle. Proliferated killer whale diety. Red, white ground, 4¾″ h. MNA
449. Double spout bottle. Proliferated, trophy head cult diety. Red, white ground, 4¾″ h. MNA
450. Mantle fragment. Border of abstracted warrior dieties holding knives and trophy heads. 6′ 6⅞″x1′ 9⅛″. TMDC
*451. Double spout bottle. Elaborate feline figure, vegetable and fruit symbols attached, border of faces. Polychrome, white ground, 8″ h. EN
452. Effigy beaker, arm holds small beaker. Polychrome, 7⅝″ h. MRI
453. Solid figure, standing male. Tan and red, 12¾″ h. MNA
454. Solid figure, standing male. Cream and red, 12¾″ h. ANON
455. Solid figure, seated female. Cream and black, traces of red and white, 11⅜″ h. ANON
456. Solid figure, standing female. Black, tan, 2½″ h. EN
457. Effigy beaker, seated figure with carrying cloth. Polychrome, 8⅝″ h. MNA
458. Effigy bottle, seated figure holding trophy head. Polychrome, 9⅛″ h. ANON
459. Effigy bottle, seated figure holding wounded knee. Polychrome, 6¼″ h. ANON
460. Beaker, representation of mountains with foxes, llamas and cactus, running warriors with feathered lances at top. Polychrome, 8⅜″ h. RA
461. Beaker, parallel zigzag lines (Op art?). Red and black on white ground, 7⅞″ h. LC
462. Double spout bottle. Elaborate ritual scene. ANON
463. Single spout bottle. Feline with protruding teeth, masked priest and other figures. Polychrome, cream ground, 6⅛″ h. RA
464. Single spout effigy bottle. Man with protruding teeth. Polychrome, 4¼″ h. ANON
*465. Double spout bottle. Feline with protruding teeth. Appears to be a late version of the feline vegetable guardian (# 562). Note attached vegetable symbols. Polychrome, 5″ h. MNA
466. Double spout bottle. Head symbols of toothy feline motif. Polychrome, 5⅛″ h. MNA

THE NAZCA WARI TRANSITION 600-700 A.D.

During the final phases of the Late Nazca period a vigorous new highland culture with its capitol at Wari near Ayacucho developed as the result of the conversion of the local Nazca-related culture to the militant religion of the Tiahuanaco people located in the southern high-plane around Lake Titicaca. The conversion must have been peaceful since Tiahuanaco ceramic types do not occur at Wari as they would have, had a conquest been involved. Tiahuanaco ceramics were thin and elegant polychrome wares (see Nos. 544–547). Wari pottery was simple in form, solidly constructed, and decorated in a few clear colors with red and orange predominant. They soon displaced late Nazca types on the south coast.

*467. Pair of llama effigy jars with typical Early Wari abstracted motifs on their sides. Wari. HYO
   A. Orangeware, cream, 4¾″ h.
   B. Tan, red and orange, 4½″ h.
468. Hawk effigy jar with similar motif on back. Polychrome, red ground, 7⅛″ h. Nazca-Wari, Nazca Valley. MNA
*469. Flask-shaped bottle. Feline head on neck, arms in relief holding stylized feline figures. Abstract motif similar to those of Nos. 467 and 468 to front. Polychrome, orange ground, 8¼″ h. South Coast Wari, Ocucaje. WG
470. Constricted rim jar with typical Wari figure and chevron motifs. Orange, red, cream, black, and grey, 3½″ h. (Grave lot with No. 517.) South Coast Wari, Ocucaje. AR
471. Miniature effigy jar. Black, white, red ground, 3⅜″ h. Nazca Wari. EN
472. Effigy jar, head spout, stylized feline motif. Polychrome, red ground, 9″ h. South Coast Wari, Ocucaje. CS
473. Bowl, four fish on interior rim. Polychrome, red and orange ground, 7⅛″ diameter. South Coast Wari, Ocucaje. AR
474. Textile, ends and corner tabs tapestry – woven with typical early Wari motifs. Geometric embroidered motifs on plain cloth center, 5′ 6½″x4′ 2½″. TG
475. Shirt, borders of stylized Wari motifs. 1′ 11⅝″ (incl. fringe)x2′ 6⅜″. MRI
476. Two coca bags tapestry-woven with Wari motifs. CS
   A. 5½x5½″.
   B. 5⅞x5¼″.
477. Fragment of hanging, eight geometricised feline figures holding trophy heads in one hand. (Compare with No. 465.) Warp and weft interlock technique, 12′ 10½″x3′ 1¼″. TMDC

THE WARI ART STYLE 600–1,000 A.D.

Wari iconography follows that of the Tiahuanaco culture quite closely and most of its motifs may be found on stone monuments at the great ruined city of Tiahuanaco in Bolivia. It is quite likely that these motifs were brought to Wari primarily on textiles. Finely woven tapestry designs of the period often follow Tiahuanaco models closely, and some motifs peculiar to these textiles are frequently seen on Wari ceramics (Nos. 479, 488, etc.) though they are not characteristic of Tiahuanaco pottery.
After the Tiahuanaco religion was firmly established at Wari the culture quickly and aggressively brought most of Peru under its control. This expansion does not appear to have been as peaceful as it evidently had been in the south coast. The subjugation of an area is usually recorded for the archeologist by a thick layer of ashes above which few vestiges of the conquered people's culture survive.
The war-like spirit of the Wari is admirably conveyed by their art style. Motifs are rendered in strong straight and curved lines accented by striking color contrasts. Craftmanship is highly competent and the total effect is one of strength and vitality. Wari ceramics of remarkable uniform quality are found throughout the area the culture once dominated. Since regional Wari styles are also found it is inferred that the highland types were for special ceremonial or official use.

530

THE WARI ART STYLE, 600–1000 A.D.

The following ten objects were found at Wari:

478. Flaring bowl, interior pouring spout, puma heads. Polychrome, black ground, 2¾″ h., 10⅞″ diameter. HYO
479. Cup, textile motif (See Nos. 527–530.) Polychrome, black ground, 4¼″ h. HYO
480. Straight sided bowl, profile heads. Polychrome, red ground, 3⅛″ h. HYO
481. Flaring bowl, hawk head with headdress. Polychrome, red ground, 2⅞″ h. HYO
482. Dog effigy bottle. Black, white, red, 5⅛″ h. HYO
483. Ceramic standing female figure. Beige and black, 8⅝″ h. HYO
484. Head jar. White, red, and black, 4⅞″ h. HYO
485. Textile strap, feline and other motifs. 26″ long. AYO
486. Wooden trumpet with carved warrior figure. 26½″ h. AYO
487. Two small turquoise figures. AYO
    A. Seated, holding cup. 1½″ h.
    B. Standing holding shield. 1½″ h.

The following ten examples from Ocucaje, and other south coast sites, have been selected for comparison with Nos. 478–487.

488. Flaring bowl, interior pouring spout, textile motif. Grey, brown ground, 3¼″ h. AC
489. Cup, puma head motif. Cream, grey, orange band on black ground, 3¾″ h. CS
490. Straight sided bowl, puma figures. Polychrome, red interior, 3⅛″ h. CS
491. Flaring bowl, puma heads with headdress. Polychrome, red ground, 3⅞″ h. CS
492. Dog effigy bottle. Black, white, red, 6″ h. MNA
493. Figure of warrior standing on boat. Beige, black, brown, red, 8⅛″ h. CS
494. Head jar, two loop handles. Brown, beige, red, white on black ground, 3⅞″ h. CS
495. Textile fragment, feline and other motifs. 1′ 4¾″x1′ 2½″ (irregular). FS
496. Wooden beaker in form of bird headed figure, 6¾″ h. PT
497. Small turquoise figure, standing warrior, 1⅜″ h. AR

These figures are found throughout Wari dominated territory.

498. Two small turquoise figures. Chicama valley, North Coast. ML
    A. Standing figure, circles on poncho, 1⅝″ h.
    B. Standing figure, chevrons on poncho, 1½″ h.

The following objects illustrate the basic motifs of the Wari religion.

499. Flask shaped effigy bottle, God head on neck, arms holding sacrificial victim in relief. Red, beige, black, grey, brown, 8¾″ h. Coyungo. Rio Grande valley. ANON
500. God on litter, hands to front once held ceremonial wands of another material. Polychrome, red ground, 10⅜″ h. Ocucaje. PT
501. Feather headdress and strap similar to that worn by # 500. South coast. Hat, 7⅜″ h., 6″ diameter. Collar, 5x10½″. TMDC
502. Seated figure holding cup (Kero) to front. Polychrome, red ground, 7⅝″ h. Ica valley. MRI
503. Four cornered, pile cloth hat similar to that worn by # 502. 5x4″. South coast. TMDC
504. Kero (traditional Tiahuanaco cup form, compare with # 544), with hawk heads and chevron motifs. Polychrome, red ground, 5⅛″ h. Cahuachi, Nazca valley. RA
505. Bottle, skull face on neck, rampant anthropomorphic puma figures. Polychrome, black ground, 6¾″ h. South coast. ANON
506. Bowl, one-half interior bears anthropomorphic puma figure, one-half geometric. Exterior, polychrome; interior, red, 3⅞″ h. Nazca valley. MRI
507. Flaring bowl, anthropomorphic puma figures holding trophy heads and ceremonial wands. Exterior, polychrome; interior, red, 3⅞″ h. Cahuachi. FT

Ceramics in the form of human figures, birds and animals were characteristic of the Wari style (see Nos. 482–484 and 492–494). The following are additional examples.

508. Ceramic fragment. Sensitively modelled head of infant. Cream and red, 2⅜″ h. (Highland Wari) Wacaurara, Dept. of Huancayo. AYO
509. Double spout head bottle. Black and red, 6¼″ h. Pachacamac, Central coast. (An important Wari ceremonial center.) MNA
510. Jar, seated man holding spondylus shell. Black, white and traces of green on buff, 8″ h. Batan Grande, Lambayeque valley. (The northernmost point on the coast from which Wari ceramics have been reported.) HZ
511. Pair effigy bottles. Seated figures, knees drawn up inside poncho. Central and side seams, necklace, and arms, painted on surface. Ocucaje. CS
    A. Orange, black, white ground, 5″ h.
    B. Orange, black, white ground, 5″h.
512. Large jar, head spout, trophy heads flanked by complex llama motifs with human hands holding fruit, feline back feet, and stylized wings. Polychrome, 33½″ h. MNA
513. Large jar, head spout, band of hand motifs. Polychrome, red ground, 35″ h. MNA
514. Fragment, head spout or large jar. Orange, 8¾″ h. Ocucaje. CS
515. Jar, head spout. Greyware, 13¼″ h. Ocucaje. CS
516. Llama head jar. Brownware, 4¾″ h. Nazca valley. MRI
517. Abstracted feline head cup. Polychrome, red ground, 4″ h. Ocucaje. AR
518. Crouching feline effigy bottle. Black, brown, white, 4⅛″ h. Ocucaje. AR
519. Bird effigy bottle. Black, white ground, 4⅝″ h. South coast. MRI

533

520. Parrot effigy bottle. Grey, red ground, 5⅛" h. South coast. YA

Textile designs were frequently used to ornament Wari ceramics (479–488). Three additional examples are listed below.

521. Bowl, tripod legs. Checkerboard and human hand motifs on interior. Black, orange, white ground, 4" h. Ocucaje. CS
522. Double spout bottle, band of stylized head and stepped spiral motifs. Polychrome, black ground, 5¾" h. Nazca valley. MRI
523. Similar to 522. Polychrome, red ground, 3⅞" h. Ocucaje. CS

WARI TEXTILES

Finely woven interlocking tapestry poncho shirts that were evidently official Wari garments have also been found in all parts of the Wari controlled area. Like Wari ceramics, they are quite uniform in quality, design and technique of manufacture. The weaving of two matched halves of the garment on an extremely broad horizontal loom appears to be a higland tradition that may have originated at Tiahuanaco. Several distinct groups of motifs occur, each evidently associated with a definite rank of official. The following examples show the principle design types listed in the order of their frequency of occurence.

524. Fragment, stepped spiral motifs in bands. 2' 6"x2' (outside measurements). Highland Wari, Tucucu, Sancos, Dept. Ayacucho (a rare example of textile survival in the highlands). AYO
525. Complete poncho shirt of same design as 524. (The garment was shortened in ancient times by removing two rows of motifs in the shoulder.) 3' 4¾"x2' 11¼". Provenience unknown. TMDC
526. Complete shirt. Paired abstracted heads and stepped spirals alternating with interlocking puma headed staff motifs. 3' 11⅝"x3' 7". Ocucaje. PT
527. Complete shirt. Same designs as 526 further abstracted and with different coolr scheme. 3' 5"x3' 4½". Hda. Montegrande, Nazca valley. MRI
528. Complete shirt, bands of four way repeat abstract motifs. 3' ⅝"x3' 5⅜". Ocucaje. PT
529. Tapestry band (for hat)?, winged figure holding baton alternating with figure standing on balsa reed boat compare with 493. 2' 2½" (plus unwoven warps 8"x4¾"). Coyungo, Rio Grande valley. TMDC

*530. One-half shirt. Band of winged anthropomorphic puma motifs holding batons. 1' 7¼"x6' 6¾". Ocucaje. CS

*531. Complete shirt. Same motif as 530 but abstracted beyond the point of easy recognition. 3' ⅛"x3' 3½". Provenience unknown. MNA

Other objects showing the treatment of the winged puma and related motifs in various media:

*532. Wood lime with stone and shell inlays. Red, green, white, 4¼" h. Provenience unknown. DS

*533. Gold headdress and costume ornaments, repoussé cut-out sheets. 33 pieces, largest 22½" long. Provenience unknown. HC

*534. Effigy jar. Red, grey, cream, and brown, 5½" h. Batan Grande, Lambayeque valley. HZ

535. Copper. Standing figure of puma headed warrior holding battle-axe and shield. 4¾" h. Wari. ML
536. Wood lime bottle, seated puma holding trophy head. 6¼" h. Inlays missing. Estaqueria, Nazca valley. HA
537. Throwing stick. Bone handle carved in form of feline holding trophy head. 18¼" h. Tambo de Perro, Nazca valley. HA
538. Diamond shaped feather mosaic ornament, skull motif. 4x3¼". South coast. ANON

The following two tapestry woven shirts belong to the last part of the Wari period. Like the official garments they were woven in two sections on a broad loom, then sewn together with the weft direction vertical on the garment.

539. Shirt, highly abstracted skull(?) motifs against a background of tuning fork-like elements. 3' 3½"x3' 3⅜". Ocucaje. PT
540. Shirt with highly colored vertical stripes and tassels at sleeves, neck and corner. 3' 2½"x2' 10¼". Chavina, Acari valley. MRI

532

534

531

A GLIMPSE OF SOUTHERN HIGHLAND STYLES

Not enough is known of the archeology of the southern highlands for us to be able to reconstruct its early history with any reasonable degree of clarity. Excavations have been conducted at Pukara, a site northwest of Lake Titicaca, revealing an early culture whose incised and slip decorated ceramics and stone sculpture show a close relationship with the Tiahuanaco culture. It has been proven to be contemporary with the early cultural stages at Tiahuanaco, Bolivia, but the relationship between the two groups is not yet understood.

PUKARA CULTURE, CA. 500–200 B.C.

541. Bowl reconstructed from large sherd. Incised and slip painted decoration of two anthropomorphic puma figures. (Compare with 530.) (Only a few small complete ceramics have so far been found of the Pukara style) 4″ h., 8¾″ diameter. MNA
542. Stone sculpture. Human figure, hands to abdomen. Rhyolite porphyry, 17¼″ h. MNA
543. Stone sculpture. Deeply weathered standing human figure. Rhyolite porphyry, 12⅝″ h. JP

TIAHUANACO CULTURE, 300–700 A.D.

544. Kero, stylized puma figure, and band of geometric motifs. Polychrome, red ground, 6⅞" h. MNA
545. Bowl, stylized puma and other motifs. Polychrome, red ground, 2⅞" h. MNA
546. Bowl, stylized hawk and other motifs. 3⅛" h., 4" diameter. MNA
547. Jar in form of bird (grebe). Black, 5⅜" h. Koati Island, Lake Titicaca. MNA
548. Jar, pitcher form with strap handle, geometric decor, 7¾" h. Post Tiahuanaco, southern highlands, ca. 1200 A.D. ANON

A FEW CENTRAL HIGHLAND EXAMPLES

Examples of Non-Wari styles from the central highlands are scarce and difficult to place in proper cultural context. The following represent a few random pieces of the jigsaw puzzle.

549. Stone vase. Basalt (?), 7¼" h. Pre-Wari, Vilcas Huaman, Dept. Ayacucho. Its close relationship in form to the Proto Nazca stone vase (#397) suggest as yet undiscovered early relationships with the south coast cultures. AYO
550. Flaring bowl, negative geometric decoration. 3" diameter. Pre-Wari. Huanca, Dept. Huancayo. HYO
551. Solid clay figurine. 5⅜" h. Late Nazca related. Huanca, Dept. Huancayo. HYO

*552. Conical based effigy jar, 2 loop handles, abstract face on neck, decorated with groups of parallel black lines. 17⅞" h. From the eastern slope of the Andes near Chilcas in the Pampas river valley. Dept. Ayacucho. AYO

552

THE EARLY LIMA STYLE, 100-700 A.D.

During the first millennium B.C., cultural development in the central coast area lagged somewhat behind that of the north and south coast zones. In the early centuries of the Christian era, however, large ceremonial centers were constructed in the Rimac and neighboring valleys by what is called the Early Lima or Maranga culture. The ceramic art of this group is less known than that of their Mochica and Nazca contemporaries, but in its own way it is their esthetic equal.

Early Lima ceramics are relatively rare in museum collections due in part to the heavy looting of cemeteries in the area during colonial times. They are a fine orangeware and combine skillful modelling with artful slip decoration.

Orangeware with cream and brown slip, unless otherwise indicated.

553. Deep bowl, interlocking serpent design. 8⅛″ h. Huaca Culebras, Chillon valley. (The ceramic is closely related in design to murals found in the same structure.) IAA
554. Double spout head bottle, snarling ocelot. 7⅞″ h. Pachicamac, Lurin valley. MNA
555. Single spout bottle, hawk with snake in its beak standing on lenticular form. 5½″ h. Pachicamac, Lurin valley. MNA
556. Double spout bottle with arched strap handle. House form, shepherd with herd of llamas one side, guard watching ocelot on other. 6⅞″ h. Rimac valley (?). ML
*557. Effigy bottle, llama with small llama at its side. Brown, red ground, 6¼″ h. Rimac valley(?). ANON
558. Single spout bottle, frog seated atop rectangular form. Orange, brown, red, 6½″ h. Nieveria, Rimac valley. AICG

557

564

CENTRAL COAST WARI STYLES, 700-1000 A.D.

Around 600 A.D., the Early Lima culture came under strong highland influence and soon its capitol Pachicamac became one of the most important Wari ceremonial centers on the coast. Typical Wari wares are found at Pachicamac, but elsewhere on the central coast ceramics showed a distinctly regional interpretation of the Wari style.

Orangeware with colored slip, unless otherwise indicated.

COASTAL WARI - RIMAC VALLEY

559. Double vessel, Kero and seated monkey. 7½" h. WG

COASTAL WARI - CHANCAY VALLEY

560. Feline effigy jar. 6¼" h. DS
561. Kero, frontal figure. 5⅛" h. RA
562. Deep flaring bowl, abstract bird motifs, 6⅛" h., 7⅞" diameter. TG
563. Deep flaring bowl, abstract bird and other motifs. 5½" h., 5¼" diameter. ANON
*564. Fragment of painted hanging. Frontal figure and abstract fish. 3' 9⅞"x3' 8". AC
565. Fragment of painted hanging. Frontal figure three standards and other motifs. 4' 8"x2' 4¾". AC
566. Effigy jar, rectangular grid painted on chest. "Teatino" style. 11⅜" h. RA
567. Hourglass-shaped beaker, lid with celt-shaped handle. "Teatino" style. 10¼" h. RA

COASTAL WARI - HUARA VALLEY

568. Tripod bowl, frontal face with plumed headdress. 3¾" h. MNA
569. Parrot effigy jar. 5¾" h. MNA
570. Bird effigy bottle. 6½" h. MNA
571. Effigy jar, double headed serpents in relief on shoulders, braids end in serpent designs. 13¾" h. WG
572. Tapestry band, standing anthropomorphic puma figures. 6' 2"x3¼". RA
573. Tapestry fragment, abstracted profile figures, border of geometric bird heads. 6½x6½". (Provenience uncertain.) AYO

COASTAL WARI - PATAVILCA VALLEY

574. Double flask form bottle with single spout. Blackware with abstracted winged anthropomorphic puma motifs in relief on each side. 10¾" h. WG

THE NORTH COAST WARI STYLE

A distinctive coastal Wari ceramic style is found in the area formerly dominated by the Mochica culture (the Casma to the Chicama Valleys). It is usually rather crudely made orangeware, densely decorated with highly stylized motifs in black and white slip. At its best it exhibits a barbaric vitality.

Our selection is non-representative in that it emphasizes sculptured forms which are relatively rare.

Orangeware with black, white, and orange slip.

575. Jar with two modelled monkeys at neck. Painted abstract fish, and other motifs (compare with 564). 12½" h. MNA
*576. Jar in form of llama skull, human head spout with two modelled monkeys holding ears. 10½" h. MNA
577. Head jar. Single spout, 7½" h. MNA
578. Effigy jar, seated man holding mirror, plucking beard with tweezers. 6⅛" h. MNA
579. Tapestry bag, elaborate seated anthropomorphic figure each side, border of bird heads on stepped triangles. Provenience unknown but quite possibly from this area. 6⅞x9⅝". WG

THE PERIOD OF KINGDOMS AND CONFEDERATIONS, 1000-1450 A.D.

Following the break up of the Wari empire the populations of groups of neighbouring coastal valleys and large highland basins were unified into a number of separate kingdoms and confederations. They varied considerably in size and prosperity but some of them on the coast achieved great advancement in social and political organization and constructed large well planned cities and ceremonial centers. By comparison with earlier epochs, the level of artistic achievement during this period generally declined but the irrepressible vitality of ancient Peruvian society continued to be expressed in a variety of regional styles.

THE CAJAMARCA STYLE, 1000-1450

Cajamarca had become the cultural center of the northern highlands during the Wari period. It continued as a focus of northern cultural activity down to the time of the conquest when it was the setting for the Incas fatal confrontation with Pizarro in 1532. The term Cajamarca is applied to a variety of related ceramic styles found over a wide area extending from the upper portions of the coastal valleys to the Marañon. Many examples found in recent years are said to have come from the vicinity of Tembladera. The Cajamarca style shows a continuation of late Recuay slip decorated creamware types modified by Wari influence.

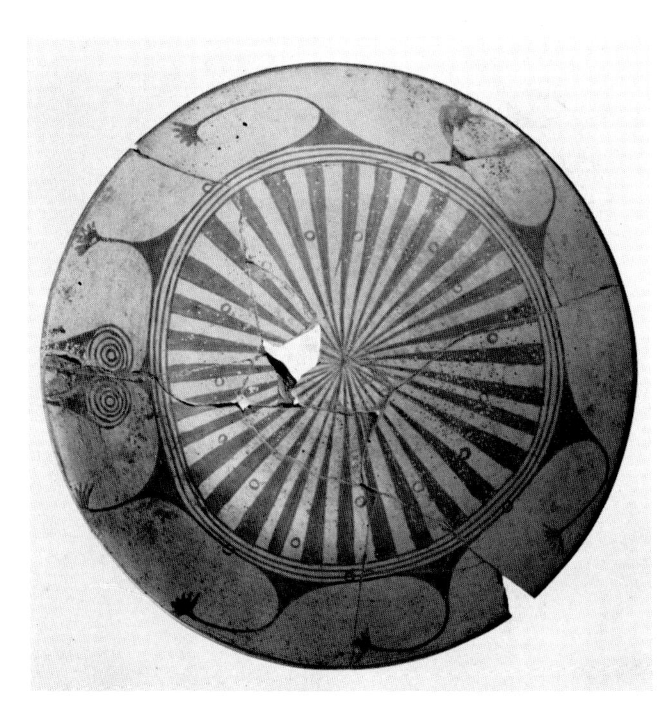

592

Creamware, slip decorated, unless otherwise indicated.

580. Three spoons decorated with curvilinear motifs. RA
    A. $3\frac{5}{8}$" long.
    B. $3\frac{3}{4}$" long.
    C. $3\frac{1}{2}$" long.
581. Kero with human face in relief, flange, geometric motifs. $5\frac{1}{2}$" h. RA
582. Bowl, curvilinear designs with abstract bird heads. $4\frac{1}{4}$" h., $6\frac{3}{8}$" diameter. RA
583. Tripod bowl, mice and rectangular panel motifs. $3\frac{1}{8}$" h. MNA
584. Tripod bowl, curvilinear motifs. Buffware, orange and black, 5" h., $5\frac{7}{8}$" diameter. ANON
585. Ring based bowl, octopus-like design on interior. $2\frac{3}{4}$" h., $7\frac{1}{8}$" diameter. MNA
586. Small ring based cup with handle. Shell form, cross hatched design. $3\frac{7}{8}$" h. Marañon valley. ANON

    The following are interior decorated ring base bowls (587-593).

587. Long tailed animal motif. $1\frac{5}{8}$" h., $4\frac{1}{2}$" diameter. ANON
588. "S" shaped reverse spirals and other motifs in quartered design. $2\frac{1}{2}$" h., $6\frac{1}{4}$" diameter. RA
589. Bisecting parallel lines with spiral appendages. $2\frac{1}{2}$" h., $6\frac{3}{8}$" diameter. RA
590. Pinwheel design. $2\frac{3}{8}$" h., $6\frac{3}{4}$" diameter. AMNH
591. Pair, possibly from Moro Ciego, Jequetepeque valley. MBL
    A. Crossed pairs of double lines with diagonal and circles at rim. $2\frac{1}{2}$" h., $5\frac{7}{8}$" diameter.
    B. Crossed pairs of double lines with round dots between. $2\frac{1}{2}$" h., $5\frac{3}{4}$" diameter.

*592. Abstract insect(?) motif, sunburst center with legs and head attached to edge. 15" diameter. JLP

593. Maltese crosses in circles with small circles forming background. 10" diameter. JLP
594. Pitcher with strap handle, two bird forms on rim, crosshatch and spirals etc. decoration. Cream and orange slip, $4\frac{5}{8}$" h. ANON
595. Similar pitcher, small circles cover surface. Cream and orange slip, $4\frac{1}{8}$" h. ANON

OTHER LATE NORTH HIGHLAND STYLES

596. Standing, hollow ceramic, male figurine. Elongated head, hands on abdomen, two holes in chest for suspension. Grey, traces of cream paint. $10\frac{1}{4}$" h. Excavated by Tello at Tantamayo, in the southern portion of the Marañon valley. MNA
597. Grotesque stone head on cylindrical shaft. Rhyolite porphyry, 35" long. Provenience and cultural affiliation unknown. MNA
598. Tenoned stone head with crested headdress. Rhyolite porphyry, $13\frac{3}{8}$" h. Huaylas style, possibly Inca contemporary. Callyon de Huaylas. MNA

THE LAMBAYEQUE KINGDOM, 700-1200 A.D.

The Lambayeque valley occupies the broad coastal plain just below the Sechura Desert on the far north coast of Peru. Actually it is a complex of three valleys incorporating the Leche and Motupe, whose rivers never reach the sea. Together they irrigate the largest single area of cultivated land in modern Peru. In ancient times the area under cultivation was much larger since today's crops of rice and sugar cane use several times the amount of water needed for pre-Columbian corn and beans.

The research of Paul Kosok and others has revealed that the ancients had also incorporated the Zaña and Jequetepeque valleys to the south into one vast irrigation network with the Lambayeque bringing over 100 miles of coastal plain under continuous cultivation. Kosok estimates that the combined area comprised one third of the cultivated land in pre-Columbian coastal Peru and supported an equal proportion of its population.

It is a surprising fact that this important zone teeming with ancient ruins, is one of the least studied and understood of all Peru. Its remoteness from Lima and its very size and complexity have discouraged archeologists. It will require a sustained program of many specialists to unveil its secrets.

Practically nothing is known of early Lambayeque history though there are indications that it shared some of the cultural trends recently discovered at Vicus. A few Mochica V ceramics have been discovered at Batan Grande in the Leche valley (# 299), along with even fewer examples of the Wari style (Nos. 510 and 533) but neither of those cultures appear to have gained much of a foothold north of the Zaña valley. The large and well organized Lambayeque population, while susceptible to outside influences, appears to have maintained its independence until around 1200 when it was incorporated into the expanding Chimu empire.

THE LAMBAYEQUE STYLE, 700-1200 A.D.

Unless otherwise indicated, the following ceramics are stirrup spout bottles in orange to buff wares decorated with fine line motifs in fugitive black and some cream paint.

599. Flaring ring base. Relief of running warrior. Traces of orange and brown paint, 7¾" h. HZ
600. Kero, with incised band at center. Painted concentric circles and plumed motifs. 5" h. HZ
601. Kero similar to 600 but with checkerboard motif and two attached modeled pepinos (fruit) decorated with bean motifs. 5" h. HZ
602. Cluster of four pepinos. Stepped crest on stirrup, wide flaring spout. 8⅜" h. MBL
603. Jar with flaring spout, and ring base. Two modeled birds, four painted birds, geometric border. 5¾" h. HZ
604. Three doves back to back. 6⅜" h. HZ
605. Figure with elaborate headdress holding discs in each hand, standing in platform with stepped parapet (see gold figure No. 618). 7½" h. Batan Grande. HZ
606. Single spout bottle with strap handle. Head spout, figures on handle, two bird flanges, 3 painted panels of warriors. 6⅝" h. ANON
607. Single spout bottle. Flaring ring base. Spout figure on litter carried by four men. Blackware, 8⅛" h. ANON
    The fine line drawings in fugitive black paint on Lambayeque pottery are often poorly preserved. It is exceptionally rare to find an exemple on which the colorful paints that were applied after firing are also preserved. (# 610.) This practice evidently had been general but ground water from infrequent rains has removed most traces.
608. Ornament (for altar?) in form of head with crested headdress. Traces of white and green paint. Black, white, cream, 8" h. HZ
609. Head ornament similar to 608 but with simple headdress and no traces of paint, 6¼" h. MBL
610. Double spout bottle with arched pierced work, bridge handle with small house form and reclining figures. Well preserved traces of cream, buff and green paints over black line motifs on body of vessel and in bands on long tapering spouts, 8¼" h. HZ
611. Fragment of painted cloth. Figures elaborate headdress holding tasseled bags. Cotton, 27½ x 27¼". TMDC

THE LAMBAYEQUE-CHIMU STYLE, 1200–1470 A.D.

*612. Double spout bottle in form of gateway guarded by soldiers. House form and reclining figures on arched handle. Orange and cream slip, 8½″ h. DS

613. Double spout vessel with 3 figures on arched strap handle. Blackware, 12″ h. MNA

614. Double vessel with whistle, cylindrical form, with relief bands, one with spout, the other with two monkeys carrying small monkey in sling litter. Orangeware, black and traces of cream paint, 7½″ h. Leche valley. MBL

615. Double vessel with whistle, one flask shaped with spout, the other cube shaped with four men carrying dead man(?) on litter. Cream and orange, 6¾″ h. Batan Grande. MBL

*616. Double vessel, one flask shaped, other seated woman holding child, monkeys on shouders. Blackware, 7″ h. SD

617. Head jar, one-eyed man with lizzard on nose. Orangeware, 6⅛″ h. HZ

Objects from the Lambayeque that are in pure Chimu style are listed under Chimu. (Nos. 640, 641, 654, and 655.)

616

612

LAMBAYEQUE GOLD, 700–1470 A.D.

619

The Lambayeque valley, especially the great ceremonial center of Batan Grande, has been the site of the largest discoveries of pre-Columbian gold in modern times. Examples are listed here without attempting to divide them between the Lambayeque and Chimu periods since the style remained essentially the same.

618. Figure with crested headdress holding discs in hands. (Was inlaid with shell or stone.) Compare with # 605. 4¼″ h., 51.8 gm. HC

*619. Disc with elaborately dressed personage holding beaker and wand. Figure is made of separate repoussé cutout sheets. 4″ diameter, 25 gm. Batan Grande. MBL

620. Four gold pins, Tucume, Leche valley. MBL
   - A. Figure related to 618 etc. 1⅞″ h., 11.5 gm.
   - B. Figure elaborate crested headdress, deer mask, holds rods in hands. 1⅞″ h., 7.45 gm.
   - C. Figure, elaborate headdress, holds drum. 1⅜″ h., 6.1 gm.
   - D. Spider with crested headdress. 1⅞″ h., 8.4 gm.

621. Necklage of 28 repoussé idols (pressed into mold). 29″ long. Batan Grande. MBL

622. 7 miniature Keros with repoussé designs of bird heads. 2″ h., 9 gm. Batan Grande. MBL

623. 3 gold Keros, Batan Grande. DS
   - A. Two repoussé bands, seated monkey figures, protruding tongues. 7⅞″ h., 4⅝″ diameter, 209 gm.
   - B. Two repoussé frontal figures holding lances. 7⅝″ h., 4½″ diameter, 208.1 gm.
   - C. Two repoussé bands elaborate wave repeat, birds and fish. 7¾″ h., 4½″ diameter, 208.1 gm

624. Kero, four repoussé frogs, four faces with crescent headdress. 5¾″ h., 5⅜″ diameter, 170.9 gm. FT

A SAMPLE FROM TUMBES

Tumbes, where Pizarro landed in 1532, is the northernmost port of modern Peru. The area is archeologically related to the great Bay of Guayaquil region of Ecuador. Though Tumbes means tombs, very few ancient art objects from the area have found their way into museums and private collections. Our single example offers a glimpse of a strange style unrelated to other Peruvian antiquities.

625. Flaring rim stand with geometric incised decor and head, tail and feet of lizzard in high relief. Buff, traces of cream, orange and black, 7⅞" h. MNA

THE CHIMU KINGDOM, 1000–1470 A.D.

The largest and most impressive ruin on the coast of Peru is Chan Chan near Trujillo which was the capitol of the Chimu, the best known of the kingdoms that formed after the collapse of the Wari empire. It was in many ways a renaissance of the Mochica culture. By the 15th century the Chimu had extended their influence throughout most of the coast of Peru and were the principle rivals of the Incas.

Chimu ceramics were predominantely blackwares and in the absence of specific knowledge there has been a tendency to lump all black ceramics under the term, especially those of diverse north costal groups which were eventually absorbed into the Chimu empire. Most of these late ceramics were mass produced and poor in quality, giving the term Chimu a connotation of artistic decadence. By careful selection, this exhibition demonstrates that Chimu art at its best is worthy of inclusion among ancient Peru's great art styles.

The sequence of Chimu art styles has not been well clarified archeologically. The tentative periods suggested below place the selected examples in what seems to be their general chronological order.

EARLY CHIMU ART, 1000–1200 A.D.

All have long tapering spouts, arched strap handles and whistles unless otherwise indicated.

626. Muffin shaped bottle with figures of three musicians. Orangeware, red and cream slip, 12″ h. MNA
627. Bird effigy bottle, beak to wing. Orangeware, red and cream slip. 9¾″ h. GG

*628. Double vessel, fish forms, bird atop one. Creamware, black line decoration, 7⅛″ h. From upper Jequetepeque valley. GG

Cajamarca influence is indicated as the source of the "North coast cursive" style which includes # 627 and the following two examples from the Moche valley.

629. Double vessel, one-half flask, other bird effigy. Orangeware, fine cursive decoration, 7⅜″ h. Moche valley. WG
630. Double vessel, cube shapes, one with four figures carrying a personage on a litter. Orangeware, cursive decoration indistinct, 7¼″ h. Chan Chan. (Compare with # 615.) SD
631. Double spout spherical bottle, flaring ring base 12 mold made frogs. Blackware, 18⅜″ h. Provenience unknown. RA

*632. Double spout bottle, lobster atop rectangular form, monkeys at base of spouts. Blackware, 6¾″ h. Chan Chan. MAT

633. Frog effigy bottle. Blackware, 5½″ h. Provenience unknown. MAT
634. Wooden idol with shell inlays, standing figure holding bowl. 13⅛″ h. From Huaca Dragon, a temple on the outskirts of Chan Chan. MAT

632

628

MIDDLE CHIMU CERAMICS, 1200–1350 A.D.

Blackwares predominate (635–639) but fine orangewares also occur (640–642).

635. Low ovoid vessel with single spout and arched strap handle to seated figure. 8″h. Chan Chan. MNA

The following, except for 635, 637 and 639, are stirrup spout bottles.

636. Seated figure of man playing flute. 9⅝″ h. Chan Chan. MAT
637. Single spout bottle, two lizzard forms on sides. 9½″ h. Chan Chan. MAT
638. Reclining deer. 8⅞″ h. Provenience unknown. MA
639. Head cup, smiling face. 3⅞″ h. Piura valley. DS
640. Seated man with deeply lined face playing pipes of Pan. Orangeware, 8″ h. Lambayeque valley(?) MNA

*641. Seated blindman eating. Orangeware, 8⅜″ h. Lambayeque valley(?) ML

642. Low ovoid capped form, birds at base of stirrups. Orangeware, 9″ h. Chicama valley. AS

WOODEN IDOLS FROM CHAN CHAN

643. Standing female figure, holds beaker in hands to front. Face painted red, 31¼″ h. MAT
644. Female figure seated crosslegged, holds beaker in hands. Deeply eaten by termites. 33¼″ h. MNA
645. Seated figure holding beaker in hands. Face painted red, originally overlaid with silver garments. 37½″ h. ML

LATE CHIMU CERAMICS, 1350–1470 A.D.

Stirrup spout bottles.

646. Two parrots seated atop cube form. Orangeware, 10⅛″ h. Provenience unknown. MNA
647. House form, relief of cats on posts, figure seated within structure, another at side. Blackware, 9⅝″ h. Chan Chan. MAT

*648. Monkey standing on all fours. Blackware, 10⅛″ h. Moche valley. MNA

649. Low ovoid form with six fruit forms attached to outer circumference. Blackware, 8⅞″. Chicama valley. ANON

641 648 741

OTHER CHIMU ART FORMS, 1000–1450 A.D.

*650. Textile hanging, warp and weft interlock technique. Geometric bird motif similar to those executed in adobe at Chan Chan. 6′ 10″ x 5′ 1¼″. AC

651. Silver bowl with cast figure of deer with bell around neck in center. 2⅛″ h., 7¾″ diameter. AC

652. Silvered copper bowl, repoussé crested animal figures, stone inlays. 2⅛″ h., 7¾″ diameter. HC

653. Feline head, copper pole finial. 3⅜″ h. WG

654. Copper disc, cast pierced work with dangles. 3⅞″ diameter. Leche valley. MBL

655. Copper disc, incised feline with human head in mouth. 3⅞″ diameter. Lambayeque valley. MBL

THE CHANCAY CULTURE, 1000–1470 A.D.

A confederation of central coast valleys, centering in the Huara and Chancay developed a distinctive culture of its own contemporary with the Chimu.

659

CHANCAY CERAMICS

Chancay ceramics, like those of the Chimu have been looked down on because of their abundance and comparatively poor workmanship. The style is primitive, almost child-like, but while it is never particularly forceful, it often has great charm. It began in early post-Wari times with the use of red and black on cream slip, but gradually dropped the red decor in favor of stark black and cream or pure cream colored wares.

656. Pair of figurines, arms raised to sides, red and black on cream. ANON
    A. Standing female. 20″ h.
    B. Standing male. 20″ h.
657. Seated female figurine, arms raised, red slipped chest, arms and head, incised band on headdress. 10⅜″ h. TG
658. Effigy jar, seated man, one hand amputated, holding panpipe to mouth with other. Flanged headdress, round ear ornaments and wide necklace. Black body, 10¾″ h. MNA
*659. Effigy jar, seated man holding cup, flanged headdress, ear spools. Black and orange on cream, 19¼″ h. Huaral, Chancay valley. FT
660. Effigy jar. Man seated on reed boat. Black on cream, 9⅞″ h. RA
*661. Jar lid. Circular disc with handle in form of a spotted feline figure tied with twisted rope to stake. Black on cream, 3¼″ h. RA

The following three examples are creamware, double vessels with long tapered spout on one, figure with whistle in head on the other.

662. Standing figure blowing flute. 8¾″ h. AC
663. Seated bird. 10⅝″ h. RA
664. Standing figure playing pipes of Pan, coffee bean eyes, incised skirt detail. 10⅜″ h. RA
665. Double vessel, jar and standing seal. Black and cream, 11½″ h. RA
666. Double vessel, flaring beaker and inverted olla form with parrot. Black, cream ground, 9″ h. RA
667. Large effigy jar, figure holding goblet, disc ornament on headdress, parrot on shoulder. Black, cream ground, 29¼″ h. SZ
668. Three undecorated flaring beakers.
    A. 8″ h.
    B. 7¾″ h.
    C. 7⅝″ h.
669. Chalice, undecorated. Cream, 5½″ h. AC
670. Pedestal base bowl with constricted rim, two modelled frogs applied. Cream, 3½″ h. AC
671. Modified hemispherical bowl with slightly constricted rim. Band of black and cream triangles, small applied decoration either side, 3⅞″ h., 6⅛″ diameter. AC
672. Shallow bowl, bisecting lines ending in half round faces. Black, cream ground, 2⅜″ h. AC
673. Standing female figure, arms raised, diagonal black lines from eyes, geometric head band. Black, cream ground, 23⅝″ h. AC

CHANCAY TEXTILES, 1000–1470 A.D.

The Chancay people were prolific weavers in a variety of techniques. Fortunately the central coast desert cemetaries provide ideal conditions for their preservation. Dyed alpaca wool was used for colored designs woven on cotton warps.

674. Tapestry hanging. Twelve large stylized jaguars with crested headdresses, four caymans. 7′ 3½″x11′ 2″. TMDC
675. Brocaded hanging, bands of anthropomorphic cats with monkey, bird and other motifs. 8′ 1¾″x5′ 3″. TG
676. Tapestry loin cloth apron with fringe. Figure with crested headdress in front of architectural setting(?). 1′ 8½″x8″. DS
677. Painted cotton panel. Zigzags and bird figures. 1′ 7¾″ x 5′ 2¼″. TG
678. Brown and white cotton double cloth panel stylized parrots. 1′ 8″x5′ 5⅝″. TG
679. Border of garment, tapestry with central motifs of "S" shaped elements composed of bird heads and plumes. 4′ 2″x 7″. TG
680. Half of a mantle showing two slit-tapestry corners. Five separately woven bands of brown and white "huck" like weave alternate with bands of two-color warp float patterning. 4′ 5½″x3′ 9¼″. TG
681. Headcloth of weft-knotted square mesh openwork, embroidered with stepped fret design. 3′ 10″x3′ 4½″. TG

CHANCAY WOODEN OBJECTS, 1000–1470 A.D.

682. Scale beam, carved and painted bird and geometric relief, cotton nets. 7⅞″ h., 6″ long. TG
*683. Standing figure with three tabbed headdress and textile garments. 34″ h. ANON
684. Figure with one arm extended to side, the other (an attached piece) to front. Face painted red. 34″ h. SZ

661

THE ICA CULTURE, 1000-1470 A.D.

690

The craft production of the late south coast Ica culture was competant but dull by comparison with the splendid art traditions that had preceded it. Textiles were usually ornamented with repetitive small figured geometric patterns and the pottery, consisting of a few rather elegant simple forms was decorated with the same motifs. Sculptured pieces were relatively rare. Our selection falls far short of representing all major types, but stresses the unusual modeled wares.

685. Cup, stylized heads and geometric motifs. Orange, black, red and cream, 3⅞″ h. ANON
686. Jar, geometric pattern and band of mice. Orangeware, cream and black, 5⅜″ h. ANON
687. Bowl, diamond textile design on exterior, stylized llamas on interior (Inca influence?). Black and orange, traces of cream, 2⅜″ h., 7¼″ diameter. ANON
688. House form, three stepped levels, modeled animal on lowest. Sides ornamented with horizontal bands of geometric decor. Cream, black, and red, 6⅞″ h. MRI
689. Female figure, hands held palms up to front. Varied geometric decor on body and headdress. Cream, black, and orange, 14⅛″ h. MNA

*690. Large jar, figure lying across top. Head forming spout, panels of textile patterns. (Reminiscent of Nazca motif of fisherman lying on nets.) Red, orange, black, and cream, 17¼″ h. MNA

691. Double vessel, cup and seated figure, bird on shoulder. Geometric decor. Red, orange, cream, and black, 6⅝″ h. Ocucaje. MRI
692. Effigy, jar, bowl on back, another held in hands arranged so liquid may flow through mouth from one bowl to the other. Red painted face, traces of black and cream, 8½″ h. Palpa valley. (Provincial Ica style.) ANON
693. Mold for making solid figurines. Redware, 8⅛ x 4″. Callango, Ica valley. MRI
694. Solid figurine, similar to mold 693. Face painted red. Black headband, cream body, 7½″ h. Santo Cristo, Nazca valley. HA
695. Three solid figurines. Buff clay, plain. SZ
    A. Seated figure. 3″ h.
    B. Seated figure. 2⅝″ h.
    C. Standing figure. 7″ h.

ICA WOODEN OBJECTS

696. Standing female figure with cradle board on back, holding male child. 8⅞″ h. FT
697. Double figure back to back, each holds trophy head. 5″ h. TG
698. Carved box for weaving tools. Frontal figures with crested headdress. 3½″ h., 8¼″ long. Ocucaje. This type of box is found throughout the coast in the late period. PT
699. Oval stool or dish with concave surface, tressel feet. 4½″ h., 14¼″ long. Hda. Tacarara, Ica valley. MRI
700. Grave post, face at top painted red. 56½″ h. MRI

ICA TEXTILES

701. Tapestry panel, 7 rows of stylized cat figures. 2′ 6⅜″ x 1′ 4⅜″. Ocucaje. PT

*702. Large Poncho type robe, frontal human and profile bird figures. Small bird motifs as space fillers. 2′ 11″x4′ 6¾″. Cahuachi, Nazca valley. MRI

702

THE INCA EMPIRE, 1470–1532 A.D.

The far-flung Inca empire encountered by the Spaniards stretched from northern Ecuador southward into Chile and Argentina, a distance of 2500 miles. It was linked together by a vast system of well constructed roads and efficiently administered by a corps of highly trained officials. It was the most extensive and best organized political unit the Americas had ever seen, yet it had begun less than a century before the Spanish arrived, and some of its territories had been incorporated in the empire for a relatively short time.

The Incas' inspired leadership constituted their chief talent. They were not innovaters, but were quick to adopt and exploit the skills of the people they conquered. Their power was absolute, but just, and their high standards brought renewed prosperity to all parts of the realm.

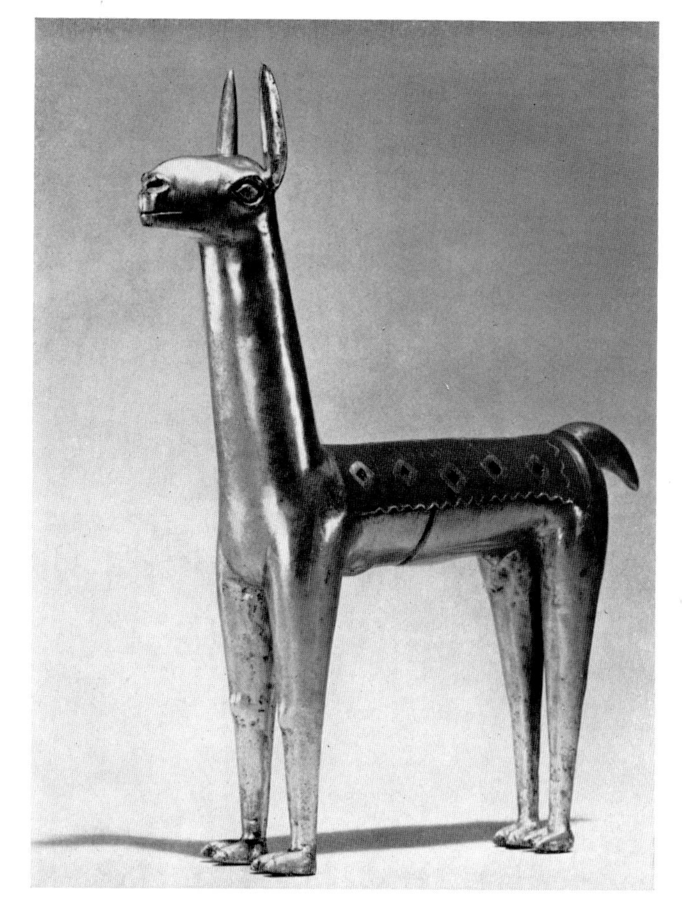

719

IMPERIAL INCA ART, 1438-1532 A.D.

The forms of Inca art were rigidly prescribed and subjected to exacting standards. So all-pervading was its influence that artifacts of the brief period are readily identifiable wherever they are encountered. It is unfortunate that we were unable to arrange loans from the University of Cuzco Museum which has the finest collection of Imperial Inca Art, but we have assembled a few outstanding examples from other sources.

IMPERIAL INCA CERAMICS

703. Aryballoid jar with geometric branching plant motif. Brown and red, 8⅛" h. Cuzco. AICG
704. Aryballoid jar similar to 703. Orangeware, red, black, and cream, 6" h. Ica valley. MRI
*705. Aryballoid jar, geometric decor. Orangeware, red, black, and cream, 8⅞"h. Island of Koati, Lake Titicaca. AMNH
706. Flaring rim jar with loop handle, geometric decor. Orangeware, red, black and cream, 12¼" h. Lake Titicaca area. AMNH
707. Straight sided bowl, two handles in the form of Pumas. Stylized headdress and geometric motifs. Red, black, orange, cream ground, 3½" h., 6" diameter. Island of Koati, Lake Titicaca. AMNH
708. Shallow tray with flaring handle. Tadpoles and catfish, pepper and seed motifs. Brown and black, 9⅜" h. Cuzco(?) AICG
709. Libation cup in form of reclining llama. Brownware, 1⅞" h., 4" long. AYO

IMPERIAL INCA STONEWORK

710. Libation cup, alpaca form. Type of soapstone, 3⅜" h. ANON
711. Libation cup, llama form. Limestone (grey), calcite (white), 5⅛" h. ANON
712. Puma, style shows Tiahuanaco influence but piece may date from colonial times. Rhyolite porphyry, 23" h., 28½" long. Cuzco. MNA

IMPERIAL INCA TEXTILES

Like their predecessor the Wari people, the Inca wove fine interlocking poncho shirts of prescribed designs for their officials. Patterns denoted rank and function.

*713. Shirt, black and white checkerboard design with red "V" yoke. 2' 11"x2' 6¾". Chavina, Acari valley. MRI
714. Shirt, checkerboard pattern of percentage sign-like motifs on yellow and black ground, horizontal bands of red and black beneath. 3' 1½"x2' 7". Inca valley. TMDC
715. Fragment of Inca shirt, stepped diamond design. 2' 6"x 10⅛". Huara valley. RA

IMPERIAL INCA STYLE METALWORK

716. Pair of hollow gold figures, Cuzco. TMDC
    A. Standing male. 2½" h., 10.3 gm.
    B. Standing female. 2⅜" h., 8.6 gm.

720

717. Solid silver female figure dressed in miniature garments and silver shawl pins. Figure 1⅜" h., dressed 2¼" h. GS
718. Solid silver female figure with horizontal bands of copper. 9⅜" h. ANON
*719. Silver llama with red lacquer inlay on saddle blanket (partly restored). 8⅞" h. AMNH
*720. Silver alpaca. 9¼" h. AMNH

705

713

738

736 758 725 *(above)*

PROVINCIAL INCA ART, 1470-1532 A.D.

Though imperial Inca art is found in all parts of the empire, each area had its own style influenced by Inca conventions such as aryballoid form and flanged spout lip, but incorporating local traditions as well. It is symbolic of the success of the administrative policies of the Incas that these local Inca period styles represented a considerable revival of regional creative genius.

THE TALLAN STYLE OF THE PIURA VALLEY

In the Piura valley there was a revival of the use of the fine clays that had been an outstanding feature of Classic Vicus ceramics. The local style called Tallan produced some of the most colorful and delightful of all Inca period ceramics.

All are stirrup spout bottles unless otherwise indicated.

721. Simple well polished bottle. Pure whiteware, 7½" h. DS
722. Two birds touching beaks. Whiteware, orange slip, 7⅜" h. DS
723. Single spout flask with loop handle. Orangeware, cream and black slip, 5⅞" h. DS
724. Long necked bird. Checkerboard wing design. Orangeware, black and cream. 6¾" h. DS

*725. Long necked bird. Creamware, orange, brown and black slip. 5⅝" h. DS

726. Duck, checkerboard wing pattern. Orangeware, cream and black slip. 6¼" h. DS

The following four ceramics are called "pachas". They were used in a water cult ceremony and are vented on both ends.

727. Aryballoid jar on digging stick. Yellow-orangeware, 3¾" h., 14" long. DS
728. Long necked bird (cormorant). Orangeware, brown slip, 6⅜" h. DS
729. Serpent. Orangeware, black and white slip, 4⅝" h. DS
730. Form of Inca tray full of corn, pineapple spout. Creamware, orange, brown and black slip, 6⅛" h. ANON

LAMBAYEQUE INCA CERAMICS, 1470-1532 A.D.

731. Jar, open mouthed puma head spout, two loop handles, cross hatch decor. Black, red and orange, cream ground, 7¾" h. Jayaca, Leche valley. MBL
732. Effigy jar, seated, wrinkled, warty dog. Creamware, 6¾" h. Provenience unknown. WG
733. Head jar, braided hair, conical cap. Orangeware, cream and black slip, 5" h. MBL
734. Modified aryballoid form, strap handle, face on neck, two bands diamond motif. Light orangeware, black and white slip, 6⅞" h. MBL
735. Aryballoid jar, neck and front panel painted with spider and fly motifs. Orangeware, cream, red, and black slip, 8" h. Cajamarca(?) MNA

*736. Drum shaped stirrup spout bottle with bird form, tail to spout, beak to drum. Orangeware, 5⅜" h. Jayanco, Leche valley. MBL

737. Llama hoof form bottle, stirrup in feline form. Mottled brownware, 7¼" h. Provenience unknown, but probably from the far north coast. EN

*738. Effigy bottle, strap handle, flaring spout. Seated female figure, child on right knee. Orangeware, black line face painting 7⅝" h. Lambayeque valley. ML

739. Effigy bottle, strap handle, flaring spout. Seated male figure carrying cluster of pots on back supported by head-band. Orangeware, cream slip, traces of black cursive designs, 8½" h. Lambayeque valley. DS
740. Tall bottle with flaring spout, three bird forms at neck. Orangeware, cream paint. Traces of black cursive designs, 10¼" h. Lambayeque valley. DS

CHIMU-INCA CERAMICS, 1470-1532 A.D.

Blackware, unless otherwise indicated.

*741. Stirrup spout bottle, bound llama. 7¼" h. WG

742. Pacha in form of monkey. 3⅜" h. WG
743. Head bottle. Thin, finely polished, 4¼" h. (Compare with silver head beakers.) WG
744. Stirrup spout bottle, bird seated on cube form. 9⅛" h. Chan Chan. MAT
745. Double vessel, spouts in form of two men carrying funerary litter. 7⅞" h. MNA
746. Double vessel, similar to 745. Base restored. Orangeware, cream slip. 6⅞" h. AC

INCA CHIMU METAL WORK, 1470-1532 A.D.

747. Pair gold figures, Huaca de la Cruz, Leche valley. (Compare with # 716.) MBL
    A. Male figure holds drum and flute, whistle in mouth. 1⅜" h., 3.5 gm.
    B. Female figure, holds trumpet and rattle. 1⅜" h., 3.75 gm.
748. Gold figure of bird, drum in one hand, stick in other. ⅞" h., 2.1 gm. Tucume, Leche valley. MBL
749. Silver head beaker. (Compare with # 743.) 8½" h. ANON
750. Wooden form over which silver head beakers were made. 5¼" h. ANON
751. Silver double faced head beaker. 12½" h., 4¼" diameter. HC

*752. Wide silvered copper and shell bead collar necklace. Mold made repoussé figures. 15⅜ x 28¼". Chilaupi, Lambayeque valley. MBL

753. Five silver "ear spoons", two pins with sculptured finials. MBL
    A. Seated monkey. 3" h., 7 gm.
    B. Standing figure. 3½" h., 8.5 gm.
    C. Bird with fish in beak. 3"h., 10.5 gm.
    D. Long beaked bird. 2" h., 5.6 gm.
    E. Long beaked bird (copper stem). 2⅜"., 4.9 gm.
    F Pin, human figure. 1" h., 1.8 gm.
    G. Pin, human head. 3⅛" h., 4.1 gm.
754. Three copper and bronze "Tumi" (chopper shaped) knives, sculptured pommels. Lambayeque valley. MBL
    A. Seated feline. Copper, 6" h.
    B. Two parrots eating corn. Bronze, 5⅜" h.
    C. Four llama heads. Bronze, copper inlays on shaft. 5¾" h.

CENTRAL COAST INCA, 1470–1532 A.D.

755. Modified aryballoid form, head on neck, arms in relief. Blackware, 7¾″ h. Pachacamac(?) AMNH
756. Double flask form bottle, bird with crayfish in beak atop one. Blackware, 6⅝″ h. Pachacamac. ANON
757. Crouching feline effigy bottle. Greyware, 5¾″ h. Provenience unknown. ANON
*758. Double vessel. house forms, figure painted on front. Bird atop one spout. Orangeware, cream and red slip, 7⅞″ h. Chancay valley(?) ANON
759. Puma effigy bottle, human face on stomach. Necklace of shell beads. Orangeware, orange, cream, and black paint, 7½″ h. Chillon valley. AMNH
760. Stirrup spout bottle, feline with human head in mouth. Orangeware, cream and black slip, 8¼″ h. Cajamaquilla, Rimac valley. DS
761. Stirrup spout bottle, man standing arms akimbo. Orangeware, cream and black slip, 7⅞″ h. Cajamaquilla, Rimac valley. DS
762. Effigy bottle, seated figure, arched headdress, elaborate ear ornaments. Orangeware, brown face paint, etc., 9⅜″ h. Provenience unknown. HYO.

SOUTH COAST INCA

763. Modified aryballoid jar with strap handle, geometric decor. Orangeware, black and red, 5½" h. Ica valley. EN
764. Modified aryballoid jar, face on neck, arms in relief. Blackware, 7½" h. Cahuachi, Nazca valley. HA
765. Effigy jar, head on neck, arms in relief. Strap handle. Blackware, 6¼" h. Provenience unknown. TG
766. Kero form with face in relief. Blackware, 5½" h. Provenience unknown. WG
767. House effigy jar, spout in typical late Ica bowl form. Blackware, 8⅛" h. Ica valley(?) ANON
768. Jar with loop handle. Geometric birds and crosses. Red, black, cream ground, 4½" h. Paradones, Nazca valley. HA

INCA WOODEN OBJECTS FROM THE ICA VALLEY, 1470–1532 A.D.

769. Steering oar for balsa raft boat(?). Pole ornamented with twenty red and yellow birds in squares. Outer row of twenty-five rats eating corn. Square pommel, geometric pierced work and eight standing red and yellow figures. 71½" long. FT
*770. Steering oar(?), paddle missing. Pole ornamented with row of ten standing figures in rectangles, outer row of ten reclining red, green and beige figures, heads raised. Square pierced work pommel with three figures performing human sacrifice at top. Red and yellow paint, 48" long. Ocucaje. CS
771. Lee board(?). Square pommel with geometric pierced work, nine standing figures at top. Six parrots on upper edge of blade. Red and yellow paint, 85" long. FT

INCA PERIOD TEXTILES FROM OCUCAJE

*772. Unfinished shirt (neck slit sewn together, side seams not joined). Fine geometric patterns in squares. 6' 5½"x2' 6". PT
773. Two ornamental slings. GS
A. ½x3⅜".
B. 1⅜x6⅜".
*774. Large hanging. Warp and weft interlock with weft brocading. Sixteen panels, cross with stepped border. 14' ½"x6' 6¾". wool. PT
775. Large hanging, diagonal rows of large stepped medallions. Multicolored with orange field, 11' 9⅛"x7' ⅝". Alpaca wool. PT

770 *(detail)*

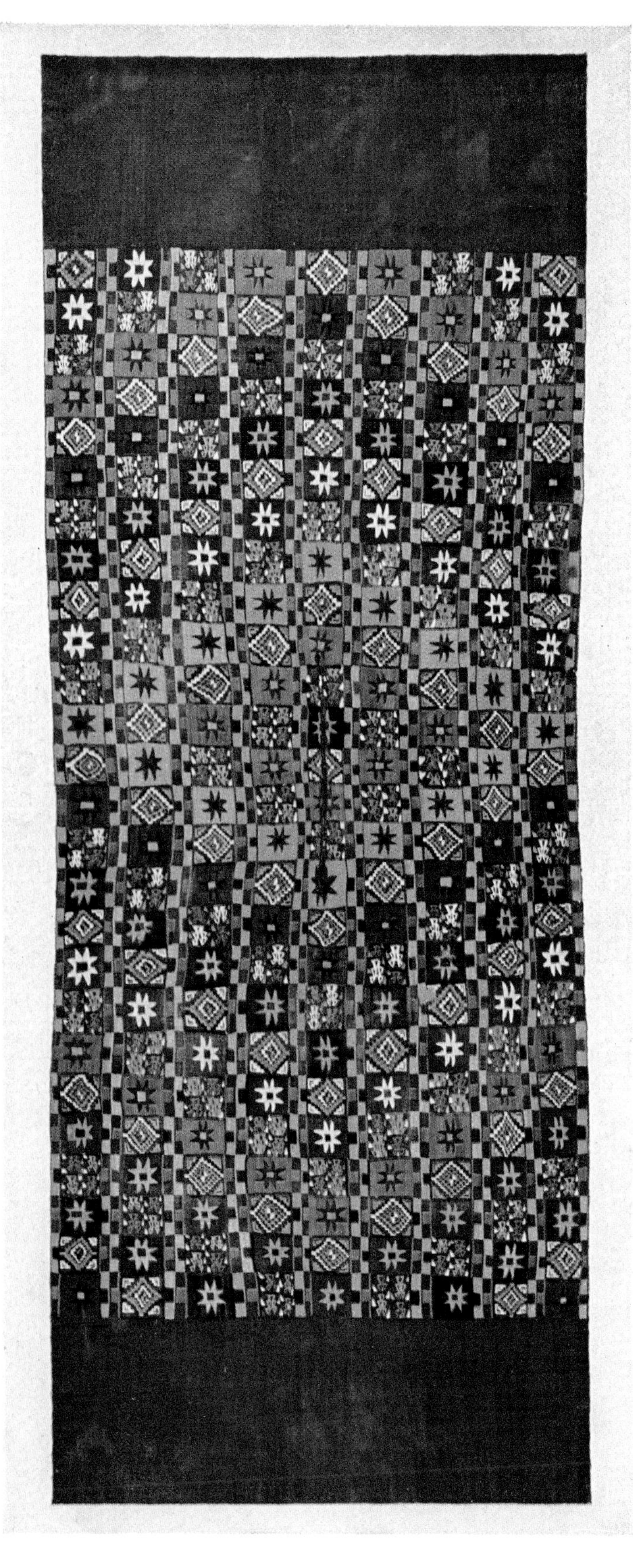

774 *(detail)*

Date / Horizon	NORTH HIGHLANDS	FAR NORTH COAST	NORTH COAST	CENTRAL COAST	SOUTH COAST	SOUTH HIGHLANDS
1532 A.D. — INCA HORIZON	INCA	TALLAN	INCA-CHIMU	INCA-CHANCAY	ICA-INCA	INCA
INCA HORIZON	CAJAMARCA	LATE CHIMU	LATE CHIMU	CHANCAY	ICA	LOCAL STYLES
		MIDDLE CHIMU	MIDDLE CHIMU			
		LAMBAYEQUE	EARLY CHIMU			
1000 A.D. — WARI HORIZON	WARI-CAJAMARCA	WARI-LAMBAYEQUE	CURSIVE	TERTINO HUARA	NAZCA-WARI 9	WARI
	RECUAY	LATE NEGATIVE VICUS	MOCHICA V	EARLY LIMA	LATE NAZCA 8 7 6	TIAHUANACO
500 A.D.		EARLY NEGATIVE VICUS	MOCHICA IV		MIDDLE NAZCA 5	
		NEGATIVE TRANSITION	MOCHICA III		EARLY NAZCA 4 3 2	LOCAL STYLES
A.D. / B.C.		CLASSICAL VICUS, VIRU PHASE	MOCHICA II	MIRAMAR		
		CLASSICAL VICUS, MATURE PHASE	MOCHICA I		PROTO NAZCA 1	
			VIRU		LATE PARACAS 10	
		CLASSICAL VICUS, CHAVINOID PHASE	SALINAR		MIDDLE PARACAS 9 8	PUCARA
	TRANSITION CHAVIN					
500 B.C. — CHAVIN HORIZON	LATE CHAVIN	TEMBLADERA	CUPISNIQUE	CURAYACU	EARLY PARACAS 7 6	
	MIDDLE CHAVIN	CHONGOYAPE			CHAVINOID-PARACAS 5 4 3 2 1	
1000 B.C.	EARLY CHAVIN					
	LOCAL STYLES	LOCAL STYLES	LOCAL STYLES	LOCAL STYLES	LOCAL STYLES	

	NORTH HIGHLANDS	FAR NORTH COAST	NORTH COAST	CENTRAL COAST	SOUTH COAST	SOUTH HIGHLANDS
INCA HORIZON	Inca-Cajamarca 735	Tallan 734	Inca-Chimu 745	Inca-Pachacamac 755	Ica-Inca 763	Imperial Inca 704
LATE PERIOD	Cajamarca 583	Lambayeque 608	Chimu 647	Chancay 662	Ica 686	Selda 552
WARI HORIZON	Wari-Recuay 225	Wari-Lambayeque 510	North Coast Wari 578	Huara 560	South Coast Wari 523	Wari 507
EARLY PERIOD	Recuay 220	Vicus Negative 175	Mochica 283	Early Lima 553	Nazca 426	Tiahuanaco 544
CHAVIN HORIZON	Chavin 22	Chongoyape 44	Cupisnique 27	Ancon 30	Paracas-Chavinoid 322	Chavinoid 74

All but the following photographs were taken by Robert E. Mates, New York:
Paul Katz, New York: Nos. 200, 282, 552, 557, 592, 616, 628, 632, 690, 705;
Textile Museum, Washington, D.C., D. L. Varela, Staff Photographer: Nos. 366, 564, 650;
Woltz Studio, Washington, D.C.: Nos. 373, 377, 530, 531, 702, 713,

Drawings by Joellyn Duesberry after designs on Peruvian ceramics: Cover and title page, details from catalique no. 272; p. 42, detail from catalogue no. 248; p. 47, detail from catalogue no. 294; p. 50, detail from catalogue no. 321; p. 54, detail from catalogue no. 321; p. 56, detail from catalogue no. 397; p. 58, detail from catalogue no. 425; p. 78, detail from catalogue no. 603; p. 111, detail from catalogue no. 221.

Maps and Charts by Arthur S. Congdon.

STAFF, THE SOLOMON R. GUGGENHEIM MUSEUM

Director	Thomas M. Messer
Curator	Louise Averill Svendsen
Associate Curator	Edward F. Fry
Assistant Curator	Diane Waldman
Research Fellow	Linda Konheim
Librarian	Mary Joan Hall
Conservation	Orrin Riley and Saul Fuerstein
Photography	Robert E. Mates
Design	Arthur S. Congdon
Registrar	Roger Anthony
Public Affairs	Robin M. Green
Publicity	Ann S. Helmuth
Membership	Istar Schwager
Business Administrator	Glenn H. Easton, Jr.
Administrative Assistant	Viola H. Gleason
Office Manager	Agnes R. Connolly
Purchasing Agent	Elizabeth M. Funghini
Sales Supervisor	Consuelo C. Murphy
Building Superintendent	Peter G. Loggin
Head Guard	George J. Sauve

Exhibition 68/6

5,000 copies of this catalogue designed by Arthur S. Congdon
have been printed by Johan Enschedé en Zonen, Haarlem, The Netherlands
in August 1968 for the Trustees of The Solomon R. Guggenheim Foundation
on the occasion of the loan exhibition "Mastercraftsmen of Ancient Peru"